Mastering
Mathematics

Teaching to transform achievement

Dr Helen Drury

OXFORD
UNIVERSITY PRESS

OXFORD
UNIVERSITY PRESS

Great Clarendon Street, Oxford, OX2 6DP,
United Kingdom

Oxford University Press is a department of the University of Oxford.
It furthers the University's objective of excellence in research, scholarship,
and education by publishing worldwide. Oxford is a registered trade mark of
Oxford University Press in the UK and in certain other countries.

British Library Cataloguing in Publication Data
Data available

978 0 19 835175 7

3 5 7 9 10 8 6 4

Paper used in the production of this book is a natural, recyclable product
made from wood grown in sustainable forests. The manufacturing process conforms
to the environmental regulations of the country of origin.

Printed in Great Britain by Bell and Bain Ltd, Glasgow

Acknowledgements
Cover photograph by shcreative

Photographs by Mel Cunningham: p. 5; shcreative: p. 9, p. 11, p. 13, p. 16, p. 19, p. 25, p. 39, p. 46,
p. 49, p. 56, p. 57, p. 60, p. 67, p. 73; Suzy Prior: p. 6-7, p. 8, p. 15, p. 21, p. 22-23, p. 24, p. 27, p. 34-35,
p. 36, p. 40, p. 47, p. 48, p. 50, p. 52-53, p. 60, p. 62, p. 64, p. 65, p. 66, p. 69, p. 72, p. 74, p. 75, p. 76;
and Smith & Scholey: p. 45, p. 70

The Publisher would like to thank the following for permission to reproduce photographs:
ARK Atwood Primary Academy; St Boniface RC Primary School; Campsbourne Infant and Junior School

The author would like to thank all the pupils and teachers
in Mathematics Mastery partnership schools and the
Mathematics Mastery team for their essential and ongoing
contribution to the development of the mastery approach.

Oxford OWL

For school
Discover eBooks, inspirational
resources, advice and support

For home
Helping your child's learning
with free eBooks, essential
tips and fun activities

www.oxfordowl.co.uk

Oxford School Improvement

Mastering Mathematics

Contents

OXFORD

UNIVERSITY PRESS

Introduction

What are children capable of achieving in mathematics? Though far from perfect, data from national assessments do give us some sense of how children in England are doing *now*. However, such data tell us almost nothing about what they might be *able* to do, given optimal conditions. We have become used to seeing roughly a fifth of children fall below national expectations by the end of primary school, with twice as many behind by age sixteen. We're accustomed to seeing two-fifths of children 'exceeding expectations' by age ten. But are these national expectations high enough? Is this distribution of achievement inevitable? Could *more* children achieve more in mathematics?

In 2012, the OECD's PISA study tested more than 510,000 students in 65 countries and economies, with a focus on mathematics.[1] Shanghai and Singapore topped the table in mathematics, with students in Shanghai scoring the equivalent of nearly three years of schooling above most OECD countries. Several other Asian countries were also in the top performing group, as well three of our European neighbours – Liechtenstein, Switzerland and the Netherlands. These findings have made national news many times – some seem to find it surprising or even depressing that we are lagging behind. To others, these stories of international success are inspiring, and show just how much children are capable of. They demonstrate that our children's current achievement in mathematics is not the best they can do; they can achieve much more.

The mastery approach is driven by a commitment to transform achievement in mathematics. Whilst every small improvement in understanding for every child merits celebration and can be transformative for that individual, the mastery approach is not just about slightly increasing the proportions who meet and exceed existing national expectations. It is driven by a determination to dramatically shift national expectations themselves, and to ensure that every single child meets them, and that many excel.

This handbook has been written for teachers and school leaders who share this commitment to transforming mathematics education. It shares some of the key principles of the mastery approach to teaching mathematics. It draws on the wide range of research that underpins the mastery approach, and uses examples of the approach in action to illustrate how teaching can be transformed and achievement raised. Teachers who teach for mastery expect every single child to succeed. This handbook introduces the frameworks and classroom approaches they use to ensure that these high expectations are met. To support its use as a professional development resource, discussion points are included at relevant points. These may provide a prompt for individual reflection, or could be used to initiate discussion in staff training.

The first chapter explores the idea of a commitment to success in mathematics for every child, and introduces the rationale for a focus on mastery. In subsequent chapters, the handbook addresses a mastery curriculum (Chapter 2), deep understanding (Chapter 3), purposeful learning (Chapter 4) and whole-school commitment and leadership (Chapter 5).

---

1   The Organisation for Economic Co-operation and Development's Programme for International Student Assessment: **OECD** (2012) PISA 2012 Results: What Students Know and Can Do: Student Performance in Mathematics, Reading and Science (Volume 1).

About the author

Dr Helen Drury has more than a decade of experience as a mathematics teacher, head of mathematics and senior leader in Oxfordshire and London. She is passionate about bringing research and best practice into the classroom to close the achievement gap and raise achievement for all. As Director of Mathematics for ARK Schools, Helen founded the charitable, not-for-profit, Mathematics Mastery partnership to build up an evidence base to demonstrate that *every* child really can succeed with mathematics, and that the high achievement of our children can rival that of children anywhere in the world. Since 2012, the collaboration has extended beyond ARK's network of schools to a large national partnership of primary and secondary member schools. These schools combine research-suggested teaching practices, professional judgement and classroom experience to collaboratively transform mathematics education.

Initially inspired by the high performance of countries such as Singapore, the underpinnings of the mastery approach provided by this handbook are theoretical and practical, local and international. It draws on national and international evidence and research findings, and is further developed through ongoing action research in schools in the UK. Throughout this handbook, examples of classroom practice are given to illustrate why or how to apply key principles of the approach. The vast majority of these examples are from the inspirational practice of schools in the Mathematics Mastery partnership, both within and beyond the ARK network of schools.

Though international successes have provided much of the inspiration, the mastery approach we explore here is grounded in UK classrooms.

In the foreword to Ofsted's Made to Measure report, Sir Michael Wilshaw stated, "We must all play our part to ensure that all of our pupils receive the best possible mathematics education."[2] This handbook introduces some of the efforts teachers and school leaders have been making to do just that, and is part of an ongoing commitment to transformation.

2   **Office for Standards in Education** (Ofsted) (2012) *Mathematics Made to Measure*. London: Ofsted.

> **"** Motivation is the most important factor in determining whether you succeed in the long run. What I mean by motivation is not only the desire to achieve, but also the love of learning, the love of challenge, and the ability to thrive on obstacles. These are the greatest gifts we can give our students. **"**
>
> *Carol Dweck*[1]

1   Dweck, C. S. (2006) *Mindset: The new psychology of success*. New York: Random House.

Chapter 1

Every Child

What's really possible?

Mastery of mathematics

Mastery is the ultimate aim of learning

The need for the term 'mastery' stems from the wide spectrum of meanings of the verb 'to learn'. If a child tells you, "today we learnt to round decimals with one decimal place to the nearest whole number", they could mean any number of things. They *might* mean that after months working with decimal numbers, they fully understand decimal place value and relative size and can give the approximate size of numbers stated as decimals. What is perhaps more likely is that they have been given a rule for rounding decimals with one decimal place, and have correctly rounded a series of these numbers. Some teachers get frustrated that a child who, having 'learnt' to round decimals in one lesson, appears to have entirely 'unlearnt' this skill by the end-of-term test, or in class the following week or even day. This happens when the focus is on 'learning' mathematics in unconnected chunks, rather than on 'mastering' the subject over time.

> In mathematics, you know you've *mastered* something when you can apply it to a totally new problem in an unfamiliar situation.

Whilst an hour's lesson might be sufficient for someone to say that they have *learnt* something, *mastery* is a much longer term investment. Let's take the example of mastering 'counting from one to ten'. A child *explores* the concept of counting by experiencing it in a wide variety of contexts. They have the skill *clarified* when an adult or another child tells them "no, eight comes after seven", or "you missed four". They *practise* counting stairs, people, biscuits and much more. Almost every lesson will offer further opportunities to *explore* the idea, moments of *clarification*, and plenty of *practice*. As the child moves to mastery of 'counting from one to ten', there will be many chances to *apply* this skill. It is through this *application* – once sufficient *exploration* and

practice have taken place and there is no longer any need for *clarification* (as no errors are made) – that the child comes to *master* the skill. As a Year 4 teacher, setting out with the intention that a class of eight- to nine-year-olds will ultimately *master* adding and subtracting fractions with the same denominator, the first thing that is clear is that this is not going to happen in sixty minutes. There may well be a lesson which begins with many children flummoxed by the question 'add two-sixths to three-sixths' and ends with them all confidently and correctly answering it – but this in itself is not necessarily a sign of successful mathematics teaching. Rather the curriculum throughout Year 4 (arguably throughout the school years) must be planned so that the necessary concepts and skills have already been explored, clarified and practised (the skill of adding positive integers, for example, and the concept of fractions) and appropriate relevant opportunities to apply the skill of adding fractions are built in to the subsequent months.

A mathematical concept or skill has been *mastered* when, through exploration, clarification, practice and application over time, a person can represent it in multiple ways, has the mathematical language to be able to communicate related ideas, and can think mathematically with the concept so that they can independently apply it to a totally new problem in an unfamiliar situation.

The 'mastery approach' that this handbook introduces is a teaching methodology that was born out of a passion for achieving mastery for every child. That *mastery* of primary mathematics is achievable by every child is therefore a key underpinning to the mastery approach.

This chapter looks at the rationale behind the mastery approach. The approach is motivated by a **commitment to transforming achievement for all**. This means placing a high value on mathematics education, adopting and promoting a growth mindset, and focusing on every child achieving a high expected standard and a high proportion excelling.

The importance of mathematics education

Mastery of primary mathematics is transformative. Children who succeed with mathematics at primary school are significantly more likely to continue their education beyond sixteen, more likely to be in employment as adults, and likely to earn more. The development of children's natural ability to think logically and solve problems is both enjoyable in its own right, and vital for success in a wide variety of fields. Inequity in the teaching of mathematics is consequently a serious social issue – every child is entitled to a high-quality mathematics education.

Numerous public statements have been made about the importance of mathematics education. Here are just a few from the last decade.

'Mathematics is of central importance to modern society. It provides the language and analytical tools underpinning much of our scientific and industrial research and development. Mathematical concepts, models and techniques are also key to many vital areas of the knowledge economy, including the finance and ICT industries. Mathematics is crucially important, too, for the employment opportunities and achievements of individual citizens.'

The Smith Report in 2004[2]

'Mathematics is essential for everyday life and understanding our world. It is also essential to science, technology and engineering, and the advances in these fields on which our economic future depends. It is therefore fundamentally important to ensure that all pupils have the best possible mathematics education. They need to understand the mathematics they learn so that they can be creative in solving problems, as well as being confident and fluent in developing and using the mathematical skills so valued by the world of industry and higher education.'

Sir Michael Wilshaw's introduction to Ofsted's 'Mathematics Made to Measure' in 2012[3]

'Mathematics is essential to everyday life, critical to science, technology and engineering, and necessary for financial literacy and most forms of employment. A high-quality mathematics education therefore provides a foundation for understanding the world, the ability to reason mathematically, an appreciation of the beauty and power of mathematics, and a sense of enjoyment and curiosity about the subject.'

Mathematics Purpose of Study, National Curriculum 2014[4]

Discussion points

Why is teaching mathematics important to you?

- Take some time to think, talk, and write about why you believe mathematics education is important.
- Write your own statement that explains your feelings about the importance of mathematics education.

2   **Smith, A.** (2004) *Making Mathematics Count: The Report of Professor Adrian Smith's Inquiry into Post-14 Mathematics Education* (2/04 937764) London, England: The Stationery Office.

3   **Office for Standards in Education (Ofsted)** (2008) *Mathematics: Understanding the Score.* London: Ofsted.
4   **Department for Education** (2014) *National Curriculum Programmes of Study.* London: Department for Education.

High expectations transform achievement

Success in mathematics, perhaps more than in other subjects, often seems to be used as an indicator of 'innate' intelligence, rather than something that everyone can achieve with effort. The current English system of teaching and assessment seems to develop a 'fixed' theory of learning[5] that results in teachers and pupils believing that they are either good at mathematics or they are not.

In my experience, every child can succeed in mathematics, whatever their socio-economic background or prior attainment, as long as they are given the appropriate learning experiences. Carol Dweck's research demonstrates that pupils and teachers who believe that intelligence is flexible, and that their goal is to learn as much as they can, are more successful than those who focus on passing exams and completing tasks.[6]

We have a responsibility to provide learning experiences that do just that and give every child the opportunity to succeed. Together with education lecturers, headteacher Alison Peacock co-authored the book 'Creating Learning without Limits', describing the positive whole-school impact of removing pre-conceived ideas.[7]

In higher performing jurisdictions, teachers, pupils and parents really care about learning mathematics. Its importance goes unquestioned, and no-one assumes that some children will inevitably struggle and fail. They believe mathematical success is possible for all.

Step into a classroom in Singapore, and it is extremely difficult to work out which 'ability' set you are observing. Teachers in every classroom act as if they expect pupils to succeed. In their first year of primary education, a small group of children are taught in an intervention class for mathematics. This is not because they'd hold the rest of the class back, or because they aren't going to keep up so there's no point in teaching them the same content as the others. Rather, it is because mathematics is viewed as so important by all involved. This intervention group follows exactly the same curriculum and content as the other children. By the end of the academic year, they are ready to join the main class, having made sense of the basics.

It's time to stop acting as if mathematics is for 'clever' people. It is *not* 'ok' to be 'bad at mathematics', but that's fine, because nobody need be in that position. Reassurance for children finding mathematics more difficult must focus on how, if they try hard, it really will all start to make sense. This will be of much more benefit to them than attempts to reassure them by claiming that it 'doesn't matter'.[8]

Of course, some children do find mathematics easier than others. But we must not underestimate the impact of quality teaching. Kurt Reusser finds sufficient evidence that most pupil underachievement is due to deficiencies in the teaching and learning environments rather than to the pupils' genetic make-up.[9] He makes the case that effective teaching positively impacts pupils' mathematics attainment levels regardless of grade levels or mathematical 'ability'.

5   Dweck, C.S. (1999) *Self-theories: Their role in motivation, personality and development.* Philadelphia: Psychology Press.
6   Dweck, C.S. (1999) *Self-theories: Their role in motivation, personality and development.* Philadelphia: Psychology Press.
7   Swann M., Peacock A., Hart, S. and Drummond, M.J. (2012) *Creating Learning without Limits.* Maidenhead: Open University Press.
8   Rattan, A., Good, C., Dweck, C.S. (2012) "'It's ok, not everyone can be good at math': Instructors with an entity theory comfort (and demotivate) students' *Journal of Experimental Social Psychology* 48, 731–737.
9   Reusser, K. (2000). Success and failure in school mathematics: Effects of instruction and school environment. *European Child & Adolescent Psychiatry, 9*(11), 17–26.

What's really possible?

What do you really believe children are capable of mathematically? Standing in front of 30-or-so children, what are your genuine expectations of what they might all achieve?

Naturally, the answer to this question will vary. My own beliefs about what children can achieve in mathematics vary day by day, lesson by lesson, task by task, or even question by question. There are of course moments when it's hard to keep expectations high. On the other hand, a great lesson, or a breakthrough comment from a child who often struggles, and anything seems possible.

This makes it even more important to really think about what genuinely *is* achievable for children's mathematics. Each of us has a 'mindset' that underlies all these in-the-moment hunches about the potential of the children we teach. It has been shown that teachers and children alike tend to maintain a consistent mindset from one year to the next.

Teachers adopting a mastery approach believe that a child's mindset is more important than prior attainment in determining the progress they will make. Pupils with a growth mindset will make better progress than pupils with a fixed mindset.[10]

Learners with a growth mindset:
- believe that effort creates success
- believe that skill and ability can be increased over time
- view mistakes as an opportunity to develop
- are resilient
- think about how they learn.

Learners with a fixed mindset:
- believe that you either have ability or you don't
- are reluctant to take on challenges
- are worried about making mistakes
- prefer to stay in their comfort zone
- think it is important to seem intelligent in front of others.

Anyone involved in primary mathematics education – teachers, teaching assistants, school leaders, family members and members of wider society – has a responsibility to aim high for every child.

'Fixed Mindset: Intelligence is a fixed trait
Growth Mindset: Intelligence is a quality that
can be changed and developed'

Carol Dweck[11]

When Shanghai or Singapore are held up as examples of what might be possible here, people point to the high levels of parental involvement, and investment in private tutoring there. As individual classroom teachers or school leaders, it can be tempting to question whether there is anything we can do.

Where individual learners have a fixed mindset, societies' expectations and values can negatively impact on their achievement. However, the evidence is emerging to show that, even where learners report that negative stereotypes are widespread in their environment, those who hold a growth mindset continue to feel that with effort they could be successful with mathematics.[12] This is exciting, as it suggests that changing the culture in the classroom may help to transform achievement even while society catches up.

10 **Dweck, C.S.** (1999) *Self-theories: Their role in motivation, personality and development* Philadelphia: Psychology Press.

11 **Dweck, C.S.** (2008) 'Can personality be changed? The role of beliefs in personality and change' *Current Directions in Psychological Science* 17:391–394.

12 See, for example, **Good, C., Rattan, A., & Dweck, C.S.** (2007) *Development of the sense of belonging to math survey for adults: A longitudinal study of women in calculus.* Unpublished manuscript.

No labels

A crucial aspect of a growth mindset is not having preconceived ideas about which pupils have more or less potential. We must think carefully about how to support pupils who find a concept difficult, and how to challenge pupils who find it more accessible, but there's no need to decide in advance which pupils this will be.

We can decide which pupils will work on which task based on observations and questioning during a lesson or series of lessons, rather than generalized assumptions about overall ability. David Hargreaves argues that ability labelling leads to "destruction of dignity so massive and pervasive that few subsequently recover from it".[13] Rather than creating 'low ability' or 'high ability' groups, we can create flexible groupings based on pupils' current depth of understanding of the relevant concept or skill.

Children whose parents have high expectations perform better: they tend to try harder, have more confidence and are more motivated to learn. While we're working on changing the mindsets of pupils, we need to make sure that all adults working with pupils have the very highest expectations for them.

At its simplest level, this means that where a pupil doesn't fully grasp a new concept at first, instead of using this to label them as a mathematical 'low achiever', the teacher tries alternative explanations and approaches. In my experience, persistent dedication to every child's success can have an impressive impact. In one very successful school, a daily twenty minute opportunity is timetabled for every teacher to meet with a small number of children who need extra support with the concepts or skills studied that morning in mathematics. These pupils are not pre-identified, but are selected based on assessment during that day's lesson. One or two children are regular attenders but every day begins

with no preconceptions about who may need help and sometimes these regulars rise to their teacher's high expectations and flourish without help. Similarly, sometimes children who generally appear to grasp new concepts quickly need a little extra support with a particular topic. Ofsted have identified this as a key contributor to pupils making outstanding progress.[14]

The effect of these 'high expectation behaviours' cannot be overstated. Put yourself in scenario A and scenario B. In which scenario are you most likely to succeed?

13 This quote is from page 62 of **Hargreaves, D.** (1982) *The challenge for the comprehensive school.* London: Routledge and Kegan Paul.

14 **Ofsted (Office for Standards in Education)** (2014) *ARK Conway Primary Academy Inspection Report* URN: 137331. OfSTED Publications.

Scenario A

You start your mathematics lesson by moving to the 'triangle table' – this is your table, and you know you are there because you are one of the worst at mathematics in the class. You know you can never be as good at mathematics as Fran, because Fran "is an octagon". After time on the carpet, you go back to your table, where you know you have been given the easiest task. Sometimes this is too easy, but you must complete it for practice. This can be frustrating if the activity on other tables looks achievable and interesting. Other times the activity is too hard. If the teaching assistant or teacher aren't too busy with others, they may come and help, but sometimes you get to the end of the lesson without really understanding. You're in an intervention group, but this has its own curriculum, unrelated to the mathematics studied in lessons.

Scenario B

You are in 'mixed prior attainment' groups, which change each half term. Your teacher takes lots of feedback during whole-class teaching and during the first activity – a paired discussion task – before setting you a task to complete. You are confident you can tackle this, as in all your mathematics lessons this year you've felt successful.

At any point, you know you can have a go at the 'super challenge' – which is available on every table in the class – so if the activity starts to seem a bit straightforward, you might give that a go. At the same time, you know that, if you struggle, you will definitely get some extra help from the teacher. Often this happens immediately. You know that by the end of the day, you will have made sense of this new mathematics concept or skill. If it doesn't happen right here and now, then time will be made for it later.

If some people are doing different tasks, you know you'll be offered an activity that is right for you (based on formative assessment during the early parts of the lesson) without any emphasis placed on whether it is relatively easy or difficult in comparison with the activities of your peers.

Although the above scenarios invited you to take the place of a child who has recently been lower attaining, the impact of these decisions have an equally detrimental impact on Fran. She may well feel that her place on the octagon table is inevitable. She may be reluctant to ask questions about why methods work, or to clarify concepts, for fear of appearing less successful at mathematics. Where she finds a concept or skill more challenging, help is less likely to be available, as adult support will mostly be targeted at the so-called 'lower groups'.

Discussion points

Think about your own classroom. Do you promote the idea that every child can succeed, or do you reinforce the idea that some are destined to excel while others will inevitably struggle? Consider:

- how children are grouped for mathematics
- how mathematics tasks are assigned to children
- how extension groups are formed
- how intervention is given.

Two ambitions

Every child: higher expectations for potential low attainers

We seem to have become used to a tail of under achievement in the UK. Other countries show us that such a tail is far from inevitable – many more children can succeed with mathematics than are doing so in the UK at the moment. Expecting that some children will struggle with mathematics quickly becomes a self-fulfilling prophecy.

A headteacher once took me to a Reception class and pointed out a little boy who was chatting with the teacher. She proudly told me how good he was at mathematics, and confidently predicted that 'he'll be one of our level 6s' – that in seven years' time, he would be exceeding national expectations in mathematics. Later in the same lesson, she drew my attention to another little boy, who she said was already struggling. 'We'll do what we can', she explained, 'but I can tell you right now that he's going to need booster classes in Year 6 – it's very unlikely he'll make level 4'.

Such judgements, made right at the start of a child's school experience, expect so little not just of these children, but also of the impact of the more than 1300 hours of mathematics education they will receive by the age of eleven. What is particularly sad is the prevalence of views and comments such as these. This headteacher is far from unusual. The process of 'formative assessment' can unintentionally result in many children being labelled as struggling with mathematics, as if there was simply nothing that could be done about it.

Yes, some children will find mathematical concepts challenging at times. Yes, some children will seem to find concepts intuitive and grasp them almost instantly. But we must stop expecting that these will always be two different groups of children. As part of learning mathematics, everyone experiences challenges and confusion at points, and everyone experiences moments of clarity and insight. It is essential that we take these moments for what they are – steps on a varied, complex and fascinating journey. Noticing such struggles and insights is important to us as teachers as it helps to inform the decisions we make about the appropriate scaffolding or challenge to provide for particular children at particular times. What these observations are not useful for is to make sweeping predictions about children's longer term success or failure with the subject.

High expectations: greater proportions of children excelling in mathematics

The mastery approach is not just about closing the gap between the highest and lowest achievers. It's about raising achievement for everyone. This not only means more children achieving the highest grades, but more children loving mathematics, more children **deeply understanding** mathematical concepts, and more children choosing to continue studying mathematics and mathematics-related subjects once it is not compulsory.

This means teaching every concept or skill in a way that promotes understanding and problem solving, so that mathematics is not just a collection of memorized techniques, but rather a coherent body of interconnected knowledge that can be flexibly applied to solve problems in unfamiliar contexts.

These two ambitions are the starting point for the concept of teaching for depth. From these two ambitions – every child succeeding, and many more excelling – come two important questions:

- What is standing in the way of 'low attainers' succeeding in mathematics?
- What are the mathematical working practices that high achieving mathematicians could do with strengthening further?

Discussion points

- What do these two ambitions mean for you and the children you teach?

- Can 'every child' mean just that, or are there any children with specific learning needs that will mean that success will need to be defined differently for them?

- What proportion of pupils will have such a deep understanding of, and enjoyment of, mathematics, that they choose to continue with the subject once it is no longer compulsory?

The mastery approach

The development of the mastery approach was motivated by the beliefs explored in this chapter. Firstly, the belief that a consistently excellent mathematics education is important both for every individual and for society. Secondly, the belief that thinking that some children are 'naturally good at mathematics', and that others are not, is a big part of the problem. Thirdly, two clear ambitions: that every child will achieve success in mathematics, and that a significant proportion will excel.

1. The mastery approach is motivated by a **commitment to transforming achievement for all**. This means placing a high value on mathematics education, adopting and promoting a growth mindset, and focusing on every child achieving a high expected standard, and a high proportion excelling.

This commitment gives rise to a series of questions:

- What curriculum structure enables every child to achieve mastery?
- What is deep understanding and how can we develop it?
- How can we plan for mastery over time?
- What is needed for a whole school to achieve mastery?

The answers to each of these questions draw on international practice, research findings and classroom experience.

Having established a commitment to transforming achievement for all, then, our next step is to consider what changes need to be made to the structure of the curriculum. Existing curriculum structures and schemes of work appear to be a barrier to achieving mastery for all. The focus of Chapter 2 is the question: **What curriculum structure enables every child to achieve mastery?**

2. The mastery approach follows a **cumulative curriculum, with sufficient time for every child to access age-appropriate concepts and skills**.

Having developed a curriculum structure that allows for, and expects, mastery for all, what teaching approaches will support teachers to achieve this? In Chapter 3 we ask: **What is deep understanding and how can we develop it?**

3. The mastery approach involves **supporting and challenging pupils through depth**. The three dimensions of depth are taken to be mathematical thinking, multiple representations, and communication.

We now need to bring together the curriculum structure with the teaching methodology. In Chapter 4 we ask: **How can we plan for mastery over time?**

4. The mastery approach involves **purposeful planning**, with clarity as to what content will be explored, clarified, practised or applied in each lesson.

Having established the motivation, curriculum, framework for depth and approach to planning, the final piece of the mastery jigsaw considers how best to put these four components into practice. Whilst an individual teacher can adopt a mastery approach, it is a challenge much better tackled as a whole school. This not only makes it easier for teachers to transform their practice, it also ensures that children benefit from a consistent approach to mathematics teaching. This leads to our fifth and final question, and the focus for Chapter 5 of this handbook: **What is needed for a whole school to achieve mastery?**

5. The mastery approach requires **transformational whole-school leadership**, with commitment to achievement, a shared approach to teaching and observation, quality training and professional learning, resourcing and planning, and mathematics celebrated and connected.

> **Show me a teacher who doesn't fail every day and I'll show you a teacher with low expectations for his or her students.**
>
> *Dylan Wiliam*

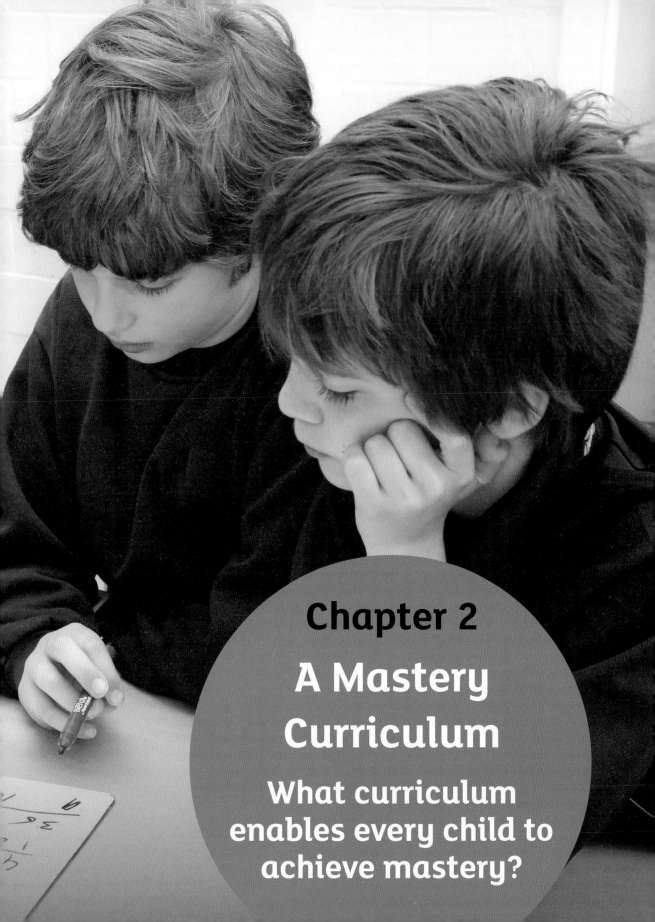

Chapter 2
A Mastery Curriculum

What curriculum enables every child to achieve mastery?

A mastery curriculum

The mastery approach follows a **cumulative, age-related curriculum for depth**. Deep understanding is promoted by planning for fewer topics. The concepts and skills studied by a child are determined by their school year, with every child in a year group studying the same concepts and skills.

Depth over coverage – a curriculum for depth

The mastery approach is not based on 'curriculum borrowing'. Whilst it is inspired by the mathematics achievement of other countries, where reference to other countries is made it is to illustrate a way in which something might work, rather than to offer evidence that it will work here. Where such evidence is offered, it is drawn from the many primary schools in England that have pioneered the mastery approach.

That said, a key difference between mathematics education in the UK and that of other, more successful, countries is the size of the mathematics curriculum. In Finland, for example, mathematics textbooks are considerably thinner than those in England. Rather than attempt to 'cover' a vast number of concepts

and skills in each year, Finnish teachers ensure their pupils have time to really master key mathematical ideas. This relatively 'small' curriculum is a consistent feature of other 'high flying' countries, including Shanghai, Singapore and Japan.

In Singapore, first year pupils spend several weeks looking at the number ten, even when many of the children can count well beyond a hundred. Countries like Singapore push children to understand these foundational concepts deeply – and they stretch the most successful pupils not by giving them the next set of numbers, but by offering them ways to explore and apply concepts, especially through problem solving.

A mastery curriculum focuses on depth of understanding rather than content coverage. All children are given time to understand something before they move on. One surprising outcome of this commitment is that teachers feel their children pick up new concepts quicker. By investing time on learning number, children as young as five have number knowledge at their fingertips. This means that when they come to a new area of mathematics, such as time or length, they are able to apply their understanding of number.

Many people have asked me how a mastery curriculum can make time for each concept or skill to be taught in depth. They wonder whether schools adopting a mastery approach have to allocate additional hours to mathematics. I do make the case for a little additional mathematics time for a daily Maths Meeting, but a mastery curriculum for mathematics is based on one daily mathematics lesson of an hour, and no curriculum content is left out. This is made possible by viewing the learning of mathematics as one coherent long-term endeavour, rather than a multitude of separate, unconnected chunks.

Mastery over time – a cumulative curriculum

Deep understanding cannot be achieved in an hour. Teachers must have a very clear purpose for each task, for each lesson, but this is very different from expecting that a particular, specified learning objective will be 'mastered' by every learner. Every moment of every lesson *is* extremely important, but important as part of a coherent long-term learning experience.

Mike Askew and other researchers at King's College London found that teachers who made connections, 'connectionist teachers', saw greater pupil progress than those who taught in a more fragmented way.[1]

They compared different teaching approaches that were more and less effective. They found that the teachers whose classes made the greatest gains across the year were those who, whatever pedagogic approach they used, emphasized connections between different mathematical ideas, between mathematics and the real world, and between the new skills and knowledge being introduced and their students' existing ideas and approaches. A mastery curriculum is structured to support teachers in making these connections.

1 Askew, M., Brown, M., Rhodes, V., Johnson, D. and Wiliam, D. (1997) *Effective teachers of numeracy.* London: King's College.

Learning mathematics is not a linear process, as Brenda Denvir and Margaret Brown demonstrate.[2] Their study finds that being immersed in one aspect of mathematics can frequently lead to unexpected learning. It is therefore not possible to map out exactly what will be *learnt* when, but it would be irresponsible not to carefully map out what will be *taught*. The mastery curriculum takes a long-term perspective, with careful consideration of the concrete and pictorial representations that will be introduced at each age, and how these will be adapted and applied in later years.

A focus on long-term orientation when considering the learning of mathematics is one of the main pedagogical principles that characterize the perspective of Hans Freudenthal. Freudenthal's learning theory underpins 'Realistic Mathematics Education' (RME) in the Netherlands, where they have a strong focus on the relation between what has been learnt earlier and what will be learnt later – longitudinal coherence.

One example of such a 'longitudinal' model in RME is the number line. It begins in the first year of school as a bead string on which the students can practise a variety of counting activities. In later years, this bead string successively becomes:

- an empty number line for supporting additions and subtractions
- a double number line for ratio problems
- a fraction/percentage bar for supporting working with fractions and percentages.

Focusing on depth enables us to carefully consider how new concepts will be represented (using concrete manipulatives and pictures or diagrams) and when abstract notation will be introduced. The concepts and skills that are taught earliest are not 'the easiest', but the ones that will be most foundational for future learning.

Mathematics learning is essentially about building connections between concepts and procedures. It's important that, as teachers, we know what the pupils have already mastered when teaching each specific topic area.

Many teachers I have worked with, have observed that a significant proportion of children lack a solid understanding of key skills in mathematics. Often, children find shape and data relatively easy, but have gaps in their understanding of the number system, e.g. a Year 6 pupil might still be using their fingers to find the sum of seven and eight, rather than recalling the number bond.

Following a cumulative curriculum addresses this by 'creating' extra time to practise and apply number skills. The skills build up over time, with teachers able to really embed a concept and build on it. In their very first year of adopting the cumulative curriculum, teachers tell me that children at their school are further ahead with mathematical understanding than they would have been this time the previous year in the same year group.

Several teachers also noted that a whole group of children that would previously have been designated as 'lower ability' or as having special educational needs, were now meeting, or even exceeding, expectations for their age.

Mastery for all – one curriculum

Higher achieving countries insist on *all* pupils reaching the same high standard. They recognize that some pupils enter without the necessary foundations in mathematics, and that time is needed to pull them up to this level. Interestingly, some of the higher performing countries do set or stream students, but placement in a 'lower' group never limits access and opportunity. In Liechtenstein, for example, all three tiers follow exactly the same curriculum content, so pupils can switch from one level to another according to performance.

2   **Denvir, B. and Brown, M.** (1986) *Understanding of Number Concepts in Low Attaining 7-9 Year Olds: parts i and ii.* Educational Studies in Mathematics, Volume 17, 15–36 and 143–164.

The highest attaining pupils study the same mathematical content as the lowest attaining – what is different is the way in which they are being taught and the level of support they are given. Every child is entitled to access the same content as their peers, and challenge is provided through increased depth, rather than acceleration of content.

Different learners do have different needs, but they do not need different content. When teaching for mastery, we do not differentiate through content. Every child is entitled to a deep understanding of the whole curriculum. This has three significant implications:

- taking things slower for everyone – spending longer with new concepts before moving on
- ensuring that even learners finding mathematics difficult access all key concepts and skills
- not 'accelerating' relatively high attainers by rushing to cover content.

As we want *every* child to succeed, we must avoid restricting pupils' progress by denying them access to key concepts and skills. Research in the 1990s demonstrated wide variation in curriculum coverage both for pupils within the same class and in different schools.[3] When we 'differentiate' by teaching different concepts to different children, we limit the achievements of children by making assumptions about their potential. It is therefore important that every child has access to the same curriculum content.

Because a mastery curriculum is cumulative, once a concept or skill has been learnt, it is built upon and applied in the learning that follows. As well as helping previously lower attaining pupils to keep up, this enables higher attaining children to gain a much deeper foundation in key concepts and skills, which better prepares them for the study of mathematics and mathematical subjects in further education and beyond.

3 **Bennett, N.** (1992) *Managing learning in the primary classroom.* Stoke: Trentham Books for the ASPE.

A mastery curriculum for Year 1

A mastery curriculum is one in which:

- there is sufficient time for each concept or skill to be understood in depth
- the content builds cumulatively throughout the year
- pupils in the same year group study the same concepts and skills.

Let's look at an example of a mastery curriculum to see these three principles in action. We will consider a mathematics curriculum for Year 1.

This was developed for schools in the Mathematics Mastery partnership and is fully aligned with the requirements of the 2014 National curriculum in England: mathematics programme of study, with slightly higher expectations in some instances. This Year 1 mastery curriculum includes every requirement from the National Curriculum for Year 1, and a small number of Year 2 requirements. These Year 2 requirements are included to help make time for place value to be fully explored by every child. This includes making time for representing 1- and 2-digit numbers across Key Stage 1.

An introduction to a Year 1 'Curriculum for Depth'		
Half term		**National Curriculum requirements**
Autumn 1	Numbers to 10	• count to ten, forwards and backwards, beginning with 0 or 1, or from any given number • count, read and write numbers to 10 in numerals and words • identify and represent numbers using objects and pictorial representations including the number line, and use the language of: equal to, more than, less than (fewer), most, least • given a number, identify one more and one less • count in multiples of twos
	Addition and subtraction within 10	• represent and use number bonds and related subtraction facts [within 10] • add and subtract one-digit ... numbers [to 10], including zero • read, write and interpret mathematical statements involving addition (+), subtraction (−) and equals (=) signs • solve one-step problems that involve addition and subtraction, using concrete objects and pictorial representations, and missing number problems

Spending the entire first half term focusing on numbers within ten may sound restrictive – but it's surprisingly liberating! By keeping the numbers relatively small, it's possible to focus on the key concepts in much greater depth. For example, the connections between number bonds and multiple number representations, and 'fact families' of addition and subtraction equations. Tempting as it may be to 'increase challenge' by using bigger numbers, in fact much greater challenge can be offered by asking rich mathematical questions about whole numbers within ten.

An introduction to a Year 1 'Curriculum for Depth'

Half term		National Curriculum requirements
Autumn 2	Shapes and patterns	<ul><li>recognize and name common 2D and 3D shapes, including: 2D shapes [for example, rectangles (including squares), circles and triangles]; 3D shapes [for example, cuboids (including cubes), pyramids and spheres</li><li>describe position, direction and movement, including whole, half, quarter and three-quarter turns</li></ul>
	Numbers to 20	<ul><li>count to twenty, forwards and backwards, beginning with 0 or 1, or from any given number</li><li>count, read and write numbers from 1 to 20 in numerals and words</li><li>identify and represent numbers using objects and pictorial representations including the number line, and use the language of: equal to, more than, less than (fewer), most, least</li><li>count in multiples of twos and fives</li></ul>
	Addition and subtraction within 20	<ul><li>represent and use number bonds and related subtraction facts within 20</li><li>add and subtract one-digit and two-digit numbers to 20, including zero</li><li>read, write and interpret mathematical statements involving addition (+), subtraction (−) and equals (=) signs</li><li>solve one-step problems that involve addition and subtraction, using concrete objects and pictorial representations, and missing number problems such as $7 = \square - 9$</li></ul>

It's important to remember that the 'Curriculum for Depth' is a cumulative curriculum. Although content relating to shapes and patterns is explicitly stated here, it is reinforced throughout Year 1. Concrete and pictorial representations of 2D and 3D shapes are used throughout the year as a context for number and measure work.

Number bonds within twenty are a key foundation for working with place value, addition and subtraction. Time spent representing and exploring these bonds is vital both for pupils to begin to understand place value of tens and units, and to commit the number bonds to memory.

An introduction to a Year 1 'Curriculum for Depth'		
Half term		**National Curriculum requirements**
Spring 1	Exploring calculation strategies within 20	• represent and use number bonds and related subtraction facts within 20 • add and subtract one-digit and two-digit numbers to 20, including zero • read, write and interpret mathematical statements involving addition (+), subtraction (−) and equals (=) signs • solve one-step problems that involve addition and subtraction, using concrete objects and pictorial representations, and missing number problems such as 7 = □ − 9
	Time	• tell the time to the hour and half past the hour and draw the hands on a clock face to show these times • recognize and use language relating to dates, including days of the week, weeks, months and years • compare, describe and solve practical problems for time [for example, quicker, slower, earlier, later] and measure and begin to record time (hours, minutes, seconds • sequence events in chronological order using language [for example, before and after, next, first, today, yesterday, tomorrow, morning, afternoon and evening]
	Numbers to 40	• count to forty, forwards and backwards, beginning with 0 or 1, or from any given number • count, read and write numbers to 40 in numerals • identify and represent numbers using objects and pictorial representations including the number line, and use the language of: equal to, more than, less than (fewer), most, least • given a number, identify one more and one less • recognize the place value of each digit in a two-digit number (tens, ones) (Y2)

This time on 'exploring calculation strategies' is time for explicitly representing and discussing strategies such as 'make ten'. These strategies will later become 'mental strategies', but at this stage it's best to resist rushing to rapid procedural fluency, as this may be at the expense of understanding. Rather than focus on the answer, the emphasis stays firmly on representing and explaining the strategies used.

This content is simply not well-suited to a one-off lesson, or even a week or fortnight of such lessons. Instead, pupils learn to tell the time through ongoing practice throughout the year. Only by revisiting this daily will these skills be fully acquired by every pupil. As a consequence, this time is not about 'learning to tell the time', but rather about beginning to solve problems involving time, and using the language of time to discuss daily events.

An introduction to a Year 1 'Curriculum for Depth'

Half term		National Curriculum requirements	
Spring 2	Adding and subtracting within 40	• represent and use number bonds and related subtraction facts within 20 • add and subtract one-digit and two-digit numbers to 20, including zero • add and subtract numbers using concrete objects, pictorial representations, and mentally, including: a two-digit number and ones; a two-digit number and tens; two two-digit numbers; adding three one-digit numbers (Y2) • read, write and interpret mathematical statements involving addition (+), subtraction (−) and equals (=) signs • solve one-step problems that involve addition and subtraction, using concrete objects and pictorial representations, and missing number problems such as 7 = □ − 9	'Within 40' might seem a somewhat arbitrary cut off, but working with numbers in the twenties and thirties helps pupils make sense of the 'teen' numbers as part of the place value system, without the overwhelming introduction of all numbers to a hundred.
	Length, weight and volume	• compare, describe and solve practical problems for: lengths and heights [for example, long/short, longer/shorter, tall/short, double/half]; mass/weight [for example, heavy/light, heavier than, lighter than]; capacity and volume [for example, full/empty, more than, less than, half, half full, quarter] • measure and begin to record the following: lengths and heights; mass/weight; capacity and volume	There are two key aspects to this part of the curriculum. Firstly practical problem solving with length, weight and volume, and secondly a chance to apply the place value, addition and subtraction concepts learnt so far in Year 1.

An introduction to a Year 1 'Curriculum for Depth'

Half term		National Curriculum requirements
Summer 1	Numbers to 100	<ul><li>count to and across 100, forwards and backwards, beginning with 0 or 1, or from any given number</li><li>count, read and write numbers from 1 to 20 in numerals and words</li><li>identify and represent numbers using objects and pictorial representations including the number line, and use the language of: equal to, more than, less than (fewer), most, least</li><li>recognize the place value of each digit in a two-digit number (tens, ones) (Y2)</li><li>identify, represent and estimate numbers to 100 using different representations (Y2)</li><li>given a number, identify one more and one less</li><li>count, read and write numbers to at least 100 in numerals</li></ul>
	Adding and subtracting within 100	<ul><li>represent and use number bonds and related subtraction facts within 20</li><li>add and subtract one-digit and two-digit numbers to 20, including zero</li><li>add and subtract numbers using concrete objects, pictorial representations, and mentally, including: a two-digit number and ones; a two-digit number and tens; two two-digit numbers; adding three one-digit numbers (Y2)</li><li>read, write and interpret mathematical statements involving addition (+), subtraction (−) and equals (=) signs</li><li>solve one-step problems that involve addition and subtraction, using concrete objects and pictorial representations, and missing number problems such as 7 = □ − 9</li></ul>

Although the National Curriculum requirements for Year 1 focus on numbers to 20, they do include counting to and across 100, and reading and writing numbers to at least 100 in numerals. The 'Curriculum for Depth' includes some Year 2 requirements in order to ensure that pupils' introduction to working with numbers to 100 focuses on representation and reinforces place value, rather than being purely procedural.

The focus throughout this challenging work on 2-digit addition and subtraction is entirely on deepening understanding of place value. No algorithms or procedures should be offered, but rather pupils explore different representations of the numbers to make sense of adding and subtracting tens and units.

An introduction to a Year 1 'Curriculum for Depth'		
Half term		**National Curriculum requirements**
Summer 2	Money	• recognize and know the value of different denominations of coins and notes • solve one-step problems that involve addition and subtraction, using concrete objects and pictorial representations, and missing number problems such as $7 = \square - 9$
	Multiplication and division	• solve one-step problems involving multiplication and division, by calculating the answer using concrete objects, pictorial representations and arrays with the support of the teacher • recognize, find and name a half as one of two equal parts of an object, shape or quantity • recognize, find and name a quarter as one of four equal parts of an object, shape or quantity

Equal and unequal grouping and sharing is part of learning in mathematics and other subjects throughout Year 1.

Discussion points

• What are the similarities and differences between this mastery curriculum and the Year 1 mathematics curriculum your school currently follows?
• What would be the challenges of adopting a mastery curriculum such as this one?
• What would be the benefits of adopting a mastery curriculum such as this one?

> **❝ I hear and I forget.
> I see and I remember.
> I do and I understand. ❞**
> – *Confucius (551–479 BC)*

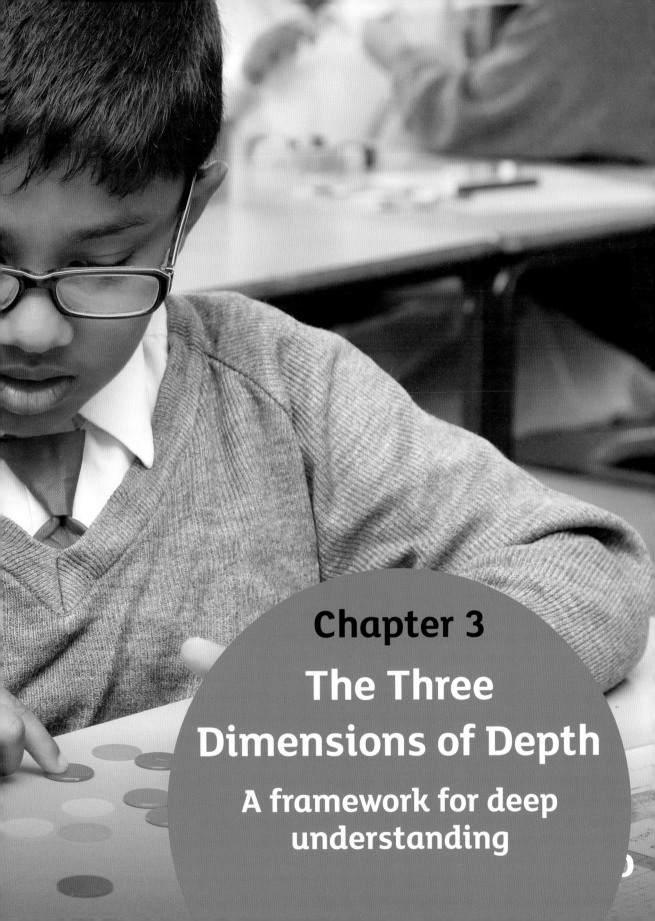

Chapter 3

The Three Dimensions of Depth

A framework for deep understanding

Deep understanding

You believe that every child can succeed in mathematics, you are prepared to commit to focusing on depth, in a curriculum that takes a long-term view, and you believe in the central role of problem solving? Great – problem solved!

If only this were true. Belief and commitment are absolutely essential to achieve success for every child, but of course they're not enough on their own.

The motivation for developing the framework introduced in this chapter was the consideration of two questions:

- What is standing in the way of 'low attainers' succeeding in mathematics?
- What are the mathematical working practices that high achieving mathematicians could do with strengthening further?

What makes the framework particularly interesting is the strong similarities between the answers to these two questions – whether struggling or excelling, all learners benefit from deepening their mathematical understanding.

There are a number of potential barriers to success in mathematics. Children can find it difficult to make sense of mathematical concepts in a meaningful way. They can struggle to verbalize their mathematical thinking. They can be challenged by such thinking itself.

To overcome these barriers, there are three key dimensions to deepening children's understanding:

- Deepening **conceptual understanding** through use of physical and diagrammatic representations, as demonstrated so effectively by countries such as Singapore and the Netherlands.
- Developing pupils' **communication**, through explicitly teaching pupils to discuss mathematics in grammatically correct full sentences with accurate terminology – a key priority in Asian countries such as Shanghai, where exposure to a more 'formal' treatment of mathematics has been credited with their success in PISA.
- Encouraging pupils to **think like mathematicians**, through giving them opportunities to seek patterns and rules, and to ask and answer open questions.

Dimensions of depth

The mastery approach places problem solving at the heart of mathematics for every child, whatever their home background or prior attainment. Every child can learn to solve complex problems in unfamiliar contexts. To enable them to achieve this, the mastery approach develops children's depth of understanding through three key dimensions: conceptual understanding, mathematical thinking and language and communication.

Conceptual understanding
Pupils deepen their understanding by representing concepts using objects and pictures, making connections between different representations and considering what different representations stress and ignore.

Conceptual understanding

Mathematical problem solving

Mathematical thinking

Language and communication

Mathematical thinking
Pupils deepen their understanding by asking and investigating great questions, by giving examples, by sorting and comparing, or by looking for patterns and rules in the mathematics they are exploring.

Language and communication
Pupils deepen their understanding by explaining, creating problems, justifying and proving using mathematical language. This use of language also acts as a scaffold for their thinking.

Dimension 1 – multiple representations

A really crucial part of a 'deep understanding' in mathematics is being able to represent ideas in many different ways. 'Representing' mathematics – using objects and pictures to represent abstract concepts – is essential for achieving mastery.

Richard Skemp describes how a 'relational' understanding of mathematics is much more powerful, long-lasting and useful than an 'instrumental' understanding.[1] Teachers in the highest achieving nations tend to focus on relationships, connections and complexities within mathematics, according to the findings of a study of seven nations.[2] An Ofsted report highlighted that: "Too often, pupils are expected to remember methods, rules and facts without grasping the underpinning concepts, making connections with earlier learning and other topics, and making sense of the mathematics so that they can use it independently."[3] An 'instrumental' understanding of mathematics – when it is seen as a set of unconnected rules to be memorized – is just as problematic for high attainers as for those who struggle. For pupils to continue with mathematics or related subjects beyond the age it is compulsory, they need to really understand it. An instrumental understanding is both less engaging, and less useful, than a relational one.

Jean Piaget describes how learning comes about through trying to make connections between our existing understanding of a concept and alternative representations for that concept.[4] The process of attempting to make these connections results in either assimilation of the new representation (if it is compatible with our existing understanding) or restructuring of our understanding to accommodate the new representation.

This resonates with the learning theory of Hans Freudenthal, who stated that,

"Instead of seeing mathematics as subject matter that has to be transmitted, I see the idea of mathematics as a 'human activity'. Education should give students the 'guided' opportunity to 're-invent' mathematics by doing it. This means that in mathematics education, the focal point should not be on mathematics as a closed system but on the activity, on the process of mathematization, going from the world of life into the world of symbols."[5]

Jean Piaget argues that children begin to understand symbols and abstract concepts only after experiencing the ideas on a concrete level.[6] Zoltan Dienes also promotes the idea that children whose mathematical learning is firmly grounded in manipulative experiences are more likely to bridge the gap between the world in which they live and the abstract world of mathematics.[7] Jerome Bruner defined three modes or systems of representation: enactive (actions), iconic (pictures) and symbolic (words, numbers and letters).[8]

1   Skemp, R.R. (1976) *Relational Understanding and Instrumental Understanding.* Mathematics Teaching, No 77, 20–26.
2   Hiebert, J., Gallimore, R., Garnier, H., Givvin, K.B., Hollingsworth, H., Jacobs, J., Chiu, A.M.Y., Wearne, D., Smith, M., Kersting, N., Manaster, A., Tseng, E., Etterbeek, W., Manaster, C., Gonzales, P., and Stigler, J. (2003) *Teaching Mathematics in Seven Countries: Results From the TIMSS 1999 Video Study* (NCES 2003-013). US Department of Education. Washington, DC: National Center for Education Statistics.
3   Office for Standards in Education (Ofsted) (2008) *Mathematics: Understanding the Score.* London: Ofsted. The quote is taken from page 5.
4   Piaget, J. (1968) *Six psychological studies.* New York: Norton.
5   Freudenthal, H. (1968). 'Why to Teach Mathematics so as to Be Useful'. *Educational Studies in Mathematics,* 1, 3–8.
6   Piaget, J. (1952). *The Child's Concept of Number.* New York: Humanities Press.
7   Dienes, Z. P. (1960) *Building Up Mathematics.* London: Hutchinson Educational Ltd.
8   Bruner, J. S. (1966) *Toward a theory of instruction.* Cambridge, MA: The Belknap Press of Harvard University Press.

When looking to deepen children's understanding of mathematics, the use of manipulatives to represent mathematical concepts and skills is a vital dimension. In the mastery approach, pupils are expected to manipulate the same concepts in a variety of ways, e.g. using cubes and beads, as well as writing and symbols. Representing ideas in multiple ways both supports low attainers to get a sense of the meaning of the abstract concept, and challenges high attainers to see a concept differently, gaining a more complete and connected perspective. Use of concrete manipulatives can make mathematics lessons practical, engaging and fun.

Mathematics is a hugely relevant subject, applicable throughout everyday life and vital to many both socially and professionally. But is this how it seems in the classroom?

There is a wealth of research in the Netherlands to demonstrate the importance of 'hands-on' learning in mathematics. Pupils manipulate objects and work with pictures and diagrams to give abstract mathematical concepts meaning and relevance.

Several studies have found that the long-term use of manipulatives (enactive learning) has a positive effect on student achievement, as the use of concrete objects allows pupils to visualize, model, and internalize abstract mathematical concepts.[9] National reports and reviews over many decades have consistently recommended that manipulatives be used to support mathematics learning.[10]

9   **Sowell, E.** (1989) Effects of manipulative materials in mathematics instruction. Journal for Research in Mathematics Education, 20, 498–505; **Ruzic, R. and O'Connell, K.** (2001). "Manipulatives" *Enhancement Literature Review*; **Heddens, J.** (1986) 'Bridging the Gap between the Concrete and the Abstract' *Arithmetic Teacher*, 33: 14–17.

10   For example, the Plowden Report, Cockcroft Report, National Numeracy Strategy Framework and Williams Review: **Central Advisory Council for Education (CACE)** (1967) *Children and their primary schools (Plowden Report)* London: HMSO **DES (Department of Education and Science)**

The value of using manipulative materials to investigate a concept, of course, depends not only on *whether* manipulatives are used, but also *how* they are used. The resources do not, in themselves, bring an understanding of mathematics. It is through interaction between children and teachers that the apparatus comes to represent a mathematical idea.[11] Used well, manipulatives can enable pupils to inquire themselves – becoming independent learners and thinkers. They can also provide a common language with which to communicate cognitive models for abstract ideas.

(1982) *Mathematics Counts: Report of the Committee of Inquiry into the Teaching of Mathematics in Schools* (Cockcroft Report). London: HMSO. Page 84. **DfEE (Department for Education and Employment)** (1999) *The National Numeracy Strategy* London: Department for Education and Employment). Page 29. **Williams, P.** (2008) *Independent Review of Mathematics Teaching in Early Years Settings and Primary Schools* London: DCSF The Association of Teachers of Mathematics, first established in 1952, was originally named the Association for Teaching Aids in Mathematics.

11 **Delaney, K.** (2001) Teaching mathematics resourcefully, in **Gates, P.** (ed.) *Issues in mathematics teaching.* London: Routledge Falmer, pp123–145. This reference is on page 124.

Many schools that have adopted a mastery approach find that the main shift in their classroom practice is not so much that they are using more concrete manipulatives – particularly at Key Stage 1, where they tend anyway to be frequently used – but that they are also making much more use of pictorial representations. This is vital for supporting children to connect the physical representations with the abstract symbols.

Recording progress

One challenge when making greater use of manipulatives is to find ways of recording pupil progress. Many of the best moments of learning aren't on paper. A teacher may witness a pupil demonstrating an understanding of a complex mathematical concept, but how is this understanding recorded?

A particularly effective way is to use photos of the mathematics pupils have engaged with. This provides a useful record for teachers and parents, as well as offering a reminder to pupils, which they can look back to.

While pupils are working independently, the teacher can circulate around the classroom with the aim of recognizing and capturing moments of understanding for every pupil. These photos can then be stuck into pupils' books with a caption explaining what the pupil has learnt.

Of course, pupils still record mathematics in their books themselves – they need to practise writing the number symbols and words – but only when it really will help their learning – when it is purposeful. They record to communicate their ideas, rather than just for the sake of it.

Differentiating using manipulatives

Manipulatives don't always make mathematics easier – if modelled correctly by the teacher, and used correctly by the pupils, they often make pupils think more deeply.

In working with pupils to develop their mathematical understanding, we can offer them concrete manipulatives, pictures and diagrams and symbolic representations.

It is rare in an effective mastery lesson to see the teacher modelling with symbols without objects or diagrams, as they would consider this a missed opportunity for depth.

Instead, you may see:

- the same manipulatives being used with different examples: e.g. lower attaining pupils may be representing examples that have already been modelled as a whole class, while higher attainers are working out how to represent new examples
- the same examples being used with different manipulatives: e.g. lower attaining pupils may be representing examples using the same manipulative that was used as a whole class, while higher attaining pupils work out how to use a new manipulative
- the same manipulatives and examples being used, but the task presented in a different way: e.g. lower attaining children might be given expressions and their representations using manipulatives, and asked to match them, while higher attainers are given only the expressions and asked to represent them with manipulatives, or vice versa.

Let's put this into action with a Year 5 class and three different lessons. In each of the three lessons, we'll differentiate a task for depth using one of the three strategies outlined above.

Converting between mixed numbers and improper fractions

Each pupil has fifteen cubes, five cubes representing one whole. They model fractions with a denominator of five, first less than, then greater than, one whole. Numbers greater than one are described as both improper fractions and mixed numbers. Pupils think of a fraction with a denominator of five, and model it for the rest of the class to guess the fraction.

The constraints then change, so that six cubes represent one whole (is each cube now worth more, or less?). After class discussion, pupils model different fractions with a denominator of six.

Let's look at the first method of differentiation for depth: the same manipulatives being used with different examples. Some pupils may continue to work with fifths and sixths, while others work with a wider range of fractions with small denominators. Pupils who are very secure might be given complete freedom over the denominators they can work with.

Limiting the range of numbers enables the teacher to further scaffold the representations, e.g. when modeling numbers with a denominator of six, pupils might have six cubes of one colour, six of a second colour, and six of a third colour. This makes the mixed number more visible. By representing eight-sixths as six red cubes and two blue cubes, pupils may 'see' that they have 'eight-sixths' (represented by the eight cubes), and also 'one and two-sixths' (the one represented by the six red cubes).

The challenge task might involve pupils generating their own examples, representing them with cubes, and writing them as a mixed number and an improper fraction. Another would be to offer pupils models already made using cubes, and for them to suggest what mixed numbers and improper fractions each model might represent.

Finding a percentage of an amount

Each pupil has a bead string (with ten groups of ten beads). We agree that the full bead string, with all one hundred beads, represents 'the whole', and use the string to model different percentages (not forgetting to include 0% and 100% and to ask about percentages greater than 100%). We then consider what 'the whole' might be. If 'the whole' was twenty-five, what would each bead represent? What's 50% of 25? 20% of 25? If 'the whole' is twenty-five, then twenty beads represents 20% of 25, which is five. The idea that something can be X% of Y, whilst also being Z, is a complex one, and merits plenty of time and exploration. We might look at thirty beads, which we agree is 30%, and think about what 30% of different amounts would be. What is 30% of 70, of 240, of 5? This might lead to a general method for finding 30% of an amount – first thinking about what ten beads (10%) represents, then multiplying this by three.

In pairs, pupils might pick a percentage card (perhaps limiting the percentages to those that are multiples of ten at this stage), and another card with an amount, and use the bead string to model how they would find the percentage of the amount.

The teacher might now choose to use the second method of differentiation for depth: the same examples being used with different manipulatives. All pupils might continue to work with finding 10%, 20%, 30%... of different amounts. Children who are finding this more difficult will continue to model the amounts and percentages using the bead string. Children who are ready for further challenge might be asked to model the percentages of amounts using a different manipulative, such as the base-ten blocks.

Reading, writing, ordering and comparing numbers with up to three decimal places

As a whole class, we might begin by looking at the number 0·926, and discussing the different ways we could represent it. Ideas might include:

- using base-ten blocks, with the single cube representing one thousandth (and so ten of the ten-by-ten cubes are needed to represent one whole)
- a really long bead string of 926 beads, where each group of ten beads represents one hundredth (and each bead represents one thousandth)
- shading a ten-by-ten grid, so that nine full rows of ten squares are shaded, plus two squares in the tenth row, plus just over half (six-tenths) of another square.

The class might then spend some time, first as a whole class and then in pairs, using one particular representation to model numbers with up to three decimal places. Let's say this is the base-ten blocks.

The teacher might then use the third option for differentiation: the same manipulatives and examples being used, but the task presented in a different way.

The challenge is to find all numbers between 0 and 1 that use only the digits 5 and 7, represent them using the base-ten blocks, and arrange them in order of size. Pupils already secure with decimal place value will need to think about how they might tackle this systematically. How will they know they've got them all? They will also need to be able to explain what the different sized blocks in each model represent.

Scaffolding for those children who need it is to start with these examples: 0·075, 0·750, 0·507, 0·75, 0·5, 0·57, 0·705

These have been chosen so that some common misconceptions can be tackled and addressed, e.g. thinking that 0·705 is greater than 0·75 because 705 is greater than 75. A pupil completing this task will effectively have made 21 comparisons (comparing 0·075 with 0·750, comparing 0·075 with 0·507, etc.), through which they will be developing a sense of the relative place value of tenths, hundredths and thousandths.

Discussion points

- Choose one of the lesson purposes. Can you think of an alternative way to differentiate the task for depth?
- Think of a different task involving manipulatives for a different lesson purpose. How could you differentiate your task for depth? What did you keep constant for every child – the type of manipulative, the examples worked with, or both?

Dimension 2 – language and communication

In the mastery approach, every single lesson has time set aside for conversation about mathematics.

Talking, reading and writing about mathematics can be really difficult. It's traditionally an abstract subject, with its own special vocabulary (a *product* isn't something to make or to buy; *sum* is more specific than it seems; even *differentiation* has its own meaning!). A study in Finland found that reading skills were a powerful predictor for mathematics performance, with the reading factor explaining 52% of the variance in mathematics performance.[12] To me, this is a powerful argument for using learning time to improve pupils' mathematical communication.

Clare Lee describes how becoming able to articulate mathematical ideas, concepts and reasoning has a profound effect on the way that pupils see themselves.[13] The better a pupil can communicate using the mathematics 'register', the more they feel themselves to be a mathematician.

Teachers who teach for mastery do not let children who are 'good at mathematics' but who struggle with English remain in the symbolic, avoiding use of words and sentences (unless it's beneficial to their learning in a particular situation). Building the foundations needed for mathematics study at A-level and beyond involves a facility to justify and prove.

Language is vital to mathematics. Mathematical modelling (consideration of a 'real-life' situation, and using mathematics to solve it) is a crucial part of the subject, and understanding and 'mathematizing' spoken and written English is vital for success with this. This starts with pupils being asked to create their own word problems, given an equation such as '6 + 7 = 13'.

Many recommendations for classroom practice are founded on a sociocultural model of education, in which talking to learn is central. These are often based on the work of Vygotsky, who argues that pupils learn through their interactions with more capable peers and adults.[14] The Cockcroft Report states that, 'The ability to 'say what you mean and mean what you say' should be one of the outcomes of good mathematics teaching. Pupils need the explicit help, which can only be given by extended discussion, to establish these relationships, even pupils whose mathematical attainment is high do not easily do this for themselves.'[15]

Celia Hoyles suggested three aspects to discussion between pupils that lead them to examine their own reasoning:

- articulating ideas brings about reflection on those ideas
- discussion involves framing ideas in a way that will be accepted by others
- listening to others modifies your own thoughts.[16]

In order to deepen children's mathematical understanding through language, teaching for

12 Korhonen, J., Linnanmäki, K., & Aunio, P. (2012) 'Language and mathematical performance: A comparison of lower secondary school students with different level of mathematical skills' *Scandinavian Journal of Educational Research,* 56(3), 333–344.

13 Lee, C. (1998) *Discussion in a Mathematics Classroom: Developing a Teacher's Awareness of the Issues and Characteristics.* Oxford: Centre for Research into Mathematics Lee, C. (2006) *Language for Learning Mathematics – assessment for learning in practice.* Buckingham: Open University Press.

14 Vygotsky, L.S. (1986) *Thought and Language.* Cambridge, MA: MIT Press.

15 DES (Department of Education and Science) (1982) *Mathematics Counts: Report of the Committee of Inquiry into the Teaching of Mathematics in Schools* (Cockcroft Report). London: HMSO, p 72.

16 Hoyles, C. (1985) 'What is the point of group discussion in mathematics?' *Educational Studies in Mathematics,* 16(2): 205–14.

mastery involves including an activity involving pupil talk, in pairs or small groups, in every single mathematics lesson. Relatively low attaining children may struggle to discuss their mathematical ideas because they lack the vocabulary, or the ability to use it in sentences. Comparatively high attaining children may feel that they can get 'the answer' on their own, and that talk is peripheral to the business of doing mathematics. Children across the full range of attainment therefore benefit from explicit modelling of mathematical talk, both to teach them its words and structures, and to demonstrate its importance.

One key way that the mastery approach emphasizes language and communication is through an insistence on complete sentences. This pedagogic technique was noticed to be effective by Doug Lemov[17]. As well as supporting pupils to construct grammatically correct sentences, this gives pupils plenty of opportunity to use mathematical terminology themselves. In the absence of this expectation, pupils might mostly experience a word such as 'equivalent' when they hear the teacher say it, or read it as part of a written mathematics question. By requesting that they speak in full sentences, pupils get the opportunity to use the words themselves and hear them used by their peers.

17 **Lemov, D**. (2010) **Teach like a champion:** 49 techniques that put students on the path to college. San Francisco: Jossey-Bass. Expecting pupils to answer in complete sentences is part of Technique 4: Format Matters, which is introduced on page 47.

In a Year 2 classroom, an exchange between teacher and pupil might go as follows:

Teacher: "What is five multiplied by six?"

Pupil: "Thirty"

Teacher: "Five multiplied by…"

Pupil: "Five multiplied by six is equal to thirty"

Other ways the teacher might remind the pupil to give a full-sentence answer include the prompt "full sentence" or a non-verbal hand signal.

As pupils' mathematical vocabulary grows, they can be encouraged to give full-sentence answers that vary the word choice from the question, e.g.

Teacher: "What is five multiplied by six?"

Pupil: "The product of five and six is thirty"

In this way, children's understanding of multiplication is deepened. I recommend a structured approach to language for mathematics, which involves cumulative mastery of vocabulary. Key words are not just listed for lessons as a one off, some never to be seen again. Many of the teachers I work with share 'star words' with the class, e.g. the words they want to hear the children using during that lesson.

> Thinking carefully not just about what mathematics you want pupils to talk about, but also about exactly what sentences and vocabulary you expect them to use to talk about it, significantly increases the chance that every child will be successful.

A number of schools have found that it is not just children's mathematics that is improving – they're having an impact on children's literacy too. This gives children a level of confidence that is born through being able to fully understand and make up their own sentences. Their deep understanding of constructing sentences soon begins to show through in all subjects, not just mathematics.

Dimension 3 – thinking mathematically

"In mathematics the ability to solve problems is not just knowing some straightforward rules"

Polya (1957)

We have considered two possible barriers to mathematical success: insufficient mathematical concept knowledge and poor mathematical communication skills. In addition to overcoming these potential hurdles, successful mathematicians have also developed mathematical 'habits of mind'. In this section we consider why mathematical thinking is the third dimension of deep understanding.

As one aim of the mastery approach is to develop a much greater number of highly able mathematicians, it is essential that children not only have deep conceptual understanding, and the ability to explain and prove mathematical ideas, but that they can generalize, specialize and seek out patterns.

Andy Noyles argues that, "many children are trained to do mathematical calculations rather than being educated to think mathematically".[18] This may well be down to the low expectations we sometimes have of pupils. It can be assumed that 'mathematical thinking' is the preserve of the lucky few – that it is somehow innate and unusual. On the contrary, such thinking is actually a very natural human behaviour. It is the role of mathematics education to develop and hone these thinking skills within every pupil.

Through studying the early language acquisition of children, Caleb Gattegno analysed four common "powers of the mind" possessed by everyone who is able to master their mother tongue[19].

These are:

- the power of extraction – finding "what is common among so large a range of variations"
- the power to make transformations – e.g., my Dad ~ my Mum's partner ~ my sister's Dad ~ my uncle's brother
- handling abstractions – e.g. any noun is a label for a general set of objects
- stressing and ignoring – e.g. focusing on one aspect of perception to the exclusion of others.

By speaking their mother tongue, children demonstrate that they already have all of these 'powers', which are so essential to mathematical thought.

Afzal Ahmed worked with teachers teaching low attaining pupils.[20] His study showed that nearly all pupils were able to use sophisticated thinking skills in learning mathematics. The teachers in the study found that pupils learnt better if they were given time to make choices, to discuss, and to explore mathematics.

18 **Noyes, A.** (2007). *Rethinking School Mathematics*. London: Paul Chapman Publishing. The quote is from page 11.
19 **Gattegno, C.**(1971) *What we owe children: the subordination of teaching to learning*. London, Routledge Kegan Paul. The 'powers' are discussed on page 9.

20 **Ahmed, A.** (1987) *Low attainers in Mathematics Project*. Better Mathematics. London: HMSO.

Reinforcing the findings of Anne Watson,[21] a study by Els de Geest and colleagues demonstrated that pupils with low prior attainment are capable of thinking mathematically, providing their teachers have high expectations of them, and put the necessary conditions in place.[22]

It is helpful to have a clear sense of what such thinking involves. Leone Burton described mathematical behaviours to pupils in her class as follows.

"Mathematicians:

- Have imaginative ideas
- Ask questions
- Make mistakes and use them to learn new things
- Are organized and systematic
- Describe, explain and discuss their work
- Look for patterns and connections
- Keep going when it is difficult

Together we can learn to be mathematicians."[23]

Al Cuoco and colleagues emphasize the critical nature of developing pupils' 'mathematical habits of mind'.[24] These habits include reasoning by continuity, looking at extreme cases, performing though experiments and using abstraction.

Anne Watson and John Mason's book *Questions and Prompts for Mathematical Thinking* provides a framework for developing such thinking in 'ordinary' lessons.[25] Great questions prompt children to:

- Think of another example
- Give a general rule
- Explain how to do a process
- Explain why a process works
- Say what is the same and what's different
- Say whether something is sometimes, always or never true

Although calculation questions (e.g. 'what is 5 x 6?') can be useful, these are more usefully asked as part of quick-fire cold calling for assessment or practice, or during Maths Meetings.

21 **Watson, A.** (2001). Low attainers exhibiting higher order mathematical thinking. *Support for Learning, 16*(4), 179–183.
22 **De Geest, E., Watson, A. and Prestage, S.** (2003) *'Thinking in ordinary lessons: what happened when nine teachers believed their failing students could think mathematically'* in Proceedings of the 27th Conference of the International Group for the Psychology in Mathematics Education Conference, Vol.2, 30–308.
23 **Leone Burton** (2004) *'Mathematicians as Enquirers: Learning about Learning Mathematics',* Springer, May 26.
24 **Cuoco, A., Goldenburg, E. and Mark, J.** (1996) *Habits of Mind: an organising principle for mathematics curricula.* Journal of Mathematical Behaviour, 15, 375–402.
25 **Watson, A. and Mason, J.** (1998) *Questions and Prompts for Mathematical Thinking.* Derby: Association of Teachers of Mathematics.

Challenging through depth

Let's take a look about how the dimensions of depth (multiple representations, language and mathematical thinking) can be put into practice.

The National Curriculum states that, in Year 3, pupils are expected to read and write numbers up to 100 in numerals and in words and add and subtract 2-digit numbers. For some Year 3 pupils, this might not seem too challenging. But have they really mastered it? Let's look at one word problem, and think about using it as a starting point for teaching for mastery in Year 3. To do this, we will incorporate multiple representations, scaffold and challenge with language, and draw on *Questions and Prompts for Mathematical Thinking* for inspiration.[26]

Our word problem is:

> There are thirty-seven bananas in a shop at the start of a week. During the week, the shop sells twenty-four bananas. Twenty-five bananas are delivered on Thursday. How many bananas are in the shop at the end of the week?

- Explain how you would solve this problem. Demonstrate using base-ten blocks.
- Can you demonstrate how you would solve this using a bead string? Using a number line?
- What is different about your explanation when you use different manipulatives?
- What stays the same about your explanation whichever manipulative you use?
- Make up another word problem that uses the same numbers and has the same answer, but in a new context. And another. And another.
- Make up a word problem that uses the same numbers and has the same answer, but that's in a context that no-one else will have thought of.

Look at this second word problem. What has changed and what has stayed the same?

> There are thirty-four bananas in a shop at the start of a week. During the week, the shop sells twenty-seven bananas. Twenty five-bananas are delivered on Thursday. How many bananas are in the shop at the end of the week?

- Solve the second problem. Is it easier or harder? Why?
- Explain how you would solve the second problem (which includes regrouping for the subtraction of twenty-seven from thirty-four). Demonstrate using base ten-blocks.
- Change one of the numbers in the second word problem to make another new problem in which you no longer need to regroup when you subtract.
- Change all of the numbers in the word problem to create a new problem where you do need to regroup.
- Can you say a rule for choosing numbers so that you do have to regroup? Can you say a rule for choosing numbers so that you don't have to regroup?
- Explain why your rule works using base-ten blocks.
- Explain why your rule works using a bead string.
- Make up and solve five word problems that are the same as this problem, but with different numbers.
- Sarah says "whatever the numbers, the shop always has more bananas at the end of the week than the start". Is this true? Is it sometimes true (or always true, or never true)?
- Can you say a rule for the numbers so that the shop has more bananas at the end of the week than at the beginning?

Discussion points

- Choose a question from an exercise or textbook for a year group you teach.
- Use the question as a starting point to create at least three different tasks designed to deepen pupils' understanding. Try to include multiple representations, scaffolding and challenge through language, and prompts for mathematical thinking.

26 Watson, A. and Mason, J. (1998) *Questions and Prompts for Mathematical Thinking.* Derby: Association of Teachers of Mathematics.

> **"** People often say: 'I teach them but they don't learn'. Well, if you know that, stop teaching. Not resign from your job: stop teaching in the way that doesn't reach people, and try to understand what there is to do... **"**
>
> *Caleb Gattegno*[1]

1   **Gattegno, C.** (1967) 'Functioning as a Mathematician' *Mathematics Teaching* 39, 6–9. Reprinted in **Brown, L., Hewitt, D. & Tahta, D.** (eds.) (1989) *A Gattegno Anthology: Selected articles by Caleb Gattegno reprinted from Mathematics Teaching*, Derby: Association of Teachers of Mathematics, pp28–9

Chapter 4

Purposeful
Learning
for Mastery

Distinguishing between a 'purpose' and a 'learning objective'

This chapter looks at planning purposeful lessons over time. Awareness of purpose is crucial when designing and facilitating opportunities for pupils to learn mathematics. Within the mastery approach, every lesson must contribute to the achievement of the long-term mission – success for every child.

The clarification of 'learning objectives' can be an excellent planning tool. Practitioners who share a clear long-term vision gain a great deal from discussing the shared medium-term objectives for a unit or term. However, where school leaders and practitioners take these long-term and medium-term objectives and attempt to allocate them, lesson by lesson, to short-term lesson plans, mathematics learning over time can often lack coherence.

Say, for example, that a class of Year 5 pupils is learning about geometry. Appropriate medium-term learning objectives for the unit might include identifying 3D shapes, estimating and comparing angles, drawing and measuring angles, and solving problems involving missing angles and sides in rectangles and regular and irregular polygons. However, when it comes to short-term planning, what a wealth of opportunities would have been lost by a two-week schedule such as follows: none of these objectives is appropriate for 'mastery' in a one hour lesson. All require a wealth of experiences, clarification, practice, and opportunities for application. It is not appropriate to have a single, or even a set of, specified learning objectives for an individual lesson – the pupils might appear to have 'met' the objective, but the learning will not be retained over time (or at least, not by everyone, and not with deep understanding).

Lesson	Learning objective
1	identify 3D shapes
2	identify 3D shapes, including cubes and other cuboids, from 2D representations
3	know angles are measured in degrees: estimate and compare acute, obtuse and reflex angles draw given acute and obtuse angles angles, and measure them in degrees (°)
4	draw given reflex angles angles, and measure them in degrees (°)
5	identify angles at a point and one whole turn (total 360°)
6	identify angles at a point on a straight line and $\frac{1}{2}$ a turn (total 180°)
7	find missing angles
8	use the properties of rectangles to deduce related facts and find missing lengths and angles
9	reason about sides and angles in regular polygons
10	reason about sides and angles in irregular polygons

In lessons 5 and 6, even if the objectives are rewritten so that the 360° and 180° are not shared with pupils at the start of the lesson, some of the potential to do mathematics by measuring angles and conjecturing about general rules seems to have been lost by stating up-front that there is a known rule to be found and memorized.

What is more, the teacher now has to work extra hard to try and re-introduce the links and connections across and beyond this area of mathematics that have been unnecessarily removed.

Instead, a mastery approach would link experiences across the lessons. So for example, hands-on experience with 3D shapes would provide a wealth of opportunities for measuring angles. Pupils could investigate when the angles on a 2D representation of a 3D shape are the same as the 3D shape itself, and when they are different. Over the course of the fortnight pupils might gradually shift from needing to measure all the angles around a point or a straight line separately, to being able to mentally calculate the last angle using angle facts. Pupils might copy 2D representations of 3D shapes by measuring lines and angles and then drawing them accurately – again, emphasizing that the 'final' angle around a point or on a straight line is predetermined by the others, and need not be measured. All this work would provide ample practice of naming 2D and 3D shapes, and hence meet all of the medium-term objectives.

There isn't anything intrinsically wrong with the list of objectives in the table opposite. Taken as medium-term objectives, they might provide a useful starting point for collaborating teachers to think about where this connects with other areas of mathematics, what mathematical habits of mind might be encouraged, what opportunities there are for links with other subjects and much more.

However, the kind of reductionist approach to identifying and discussing the purpose of a lesson exemplified through the plan can do more harm than good.

Of course, purposeful learning is absolutely vital; for each task, there must be a clear purpose. Often this will be best expressed through the way the tasks are introduced, rather than 'shared' as a statement to be read or even copied.

This purpose must be everyone's purpose. If something is so significant and important that there are some people in the class that are learning it, then why wouldn't everyone be learning it?

Discussion points

- How is a task's 'purpose' the same as and different from a learning objective?
- What might a task's purpose be?
- Might there be different kinds of task purpose?
- What are the different purposes that you might have?

We now look at four key possible types of purpose for a mathematical task: **exploration**, **clarification**, **practice** and **application**. Take the example of an eight-year-old, Jen, learning about equivalent fractions.

Learners *explore* mathematical concepts and techniques

Jen finds three red and five blue cubes. She knows that this could represent the fraction $\frac{3}{8}$, as three out of the eight cubes are red cubes. She explores different ways of representing the fraction $\frac{3}{8}$ using cubes, including six red and ten blue cubes; nine red cubes and twenty-four cubes altogether.

Learners **clarify** meanings and methods

Jen's teacher introduces the term 'equivalent' in the context of fractions, as meaning 'fractions that look different but that have the same value'. She is able to connect this term with her experiences of fractions and of equivalence – she is already aware that different fractions can represent the same number or operator.

Learners *practise* techniques

Jen develops fluency in multiplying or dividing the numerator and denominator by the same number through experiencing it on numerous occasions.

Learners *apply* concepts and techniques to solve non-routine problems

Jen is learning that the Egyptians expressed all fractions as unit fractions or as sums of unit fractions, e.g. they wrote $\frac{2}{3}$ as $\frac{1}{2}$ plus $\frac{1}{6}$. Jen finds different ways of expressing fractions as unit fractions, and considers whether it is always possible to express a fraction as the sum of two unit fractions.

Discussion points

Think of a time you have given or received feedback about an observed lesson, and disagreed about the appropriateness of a task.

- What made you think the task was or wasn't appropriate?
- Were you both clear about what the intended purpose of the task was?
- Was there a different task that would have better met the intended purpose?

In my experience, a lack of agreement about the success of a task or lesson often comes down to lack of clarity about purpose, e.g. the observer thinks the teacher should have clarified a point, but the teacher wanted to leave learners to discover and resolve the misunderstanding for themselves. Over time, pupils need a wealth of opportunities to explore mathematical ideas, to have these ideas clarified, to practise using skills and concepts, and to apply them to new contexts. This cannot all happen in a single task or lesson. It is therefore helpful to be explicit about lesson purpose when planning, teaching, and reflecting on learning.

In order to fully master a mathematical concept or technique, learners must have multiple opportunities to **explore**, **clarify**, **practise** and **apply** it. There is really no 'correct order' to these four foci for learning, which often occur in combination or are spontaneous.

Children starting formal education from comparatively supportive backgrounds may not only have had significantly greater opportunities to explore mathematical ideas (e.g. playing with blocks) but possibly also greater clarity (what's the next number after eleven? Does it really go twenty-nine, twenty-ten?), practice (let's see if we can count to twenty before Jane gets back) and application (do we have enough cakes for everyone to have two each? How could we check?).

In working with those children at risk of underachieving in mathematics, therefore, we need to ensure that we compensate for the opportunities they may have missed in early childhood. When beginning to work with a new concept, children from more supported backgrounds may be more confident to gloss over any gaps in their exploration, clarification, practice or application, simply because the foundations of number sense on which they are building are so much stronger. Children from less mathematically supportive backgrounds need to have these more carefully planned.

Adapting a task for the purpose of exploration:

- make a note of misconceptions, but do not inevitably intervene – through further exploration learners may come to be aware of the errors in their thinking, and re-conceptualize for themselves
- **Assessing for exploration** – do the pupils demonstrate commitment to exploring mathematics?

Adapting a task for the purpose of clarification:

- recognize that the clarification might more effectively come from peers or from engagement with the task, rather than from you as the teacher. This must be well-planned and cannot be left to chance.
- **Assessing for clarification** – what misconceptions do pupils demonstrate?

Adapting a task for the purpose of practice:

- 'perfect practice makes perfect' – if the purpose is practice (not exploration) then no errors should be made by learners – otherwise they will be 'mastering' a misconception or an incorrect technique.
- **Assessing for practice** – immediate assessment and intervention – "perfect practice makes perfect" – if pupils practise errors, they will become learnt errors.

Adapting a task for the purpose of application:

- resist the temptation to make clear the concept or technique to be applied (e.g. by including it in a shared learning objective, or by the timing of the task or lesson), as connecting the non-routine problem in the unfamiliar context to the previously learnt concept is vital to application.
- **Assessing for application** – how much scaffolding do pupils need to identify the concepts and techniques needed to solve the problem?

The experiences of the eight-year-old Jen could be conceived as all taking place during one mathematics lesson. However, it is often the case that such structures lead to rushing 'apparent mastery' rather than allowing time for learners to achieve genuine mastery.

If Jen benefits from numerous experiences of *exploring* the concept of equivalent fractions long before she clarifies or practises the concept, and numerous experiences of *applying* the concept once she has clarified and practised it, then her understanding of equivalent fractions will be much the deeper for it.

What does this all mean for the class of nine- and ten-year-olds learning geometry? Firstly, that they may have had experience, clarification and practice of much of this content already in their Maths Meetings. They may even have identified angles round a point and on a straight line, approximated and compared angle sizes – and if they haven't this will certainly be incorporated into their Maths Meetings during and after this unit.

Looking at the ten learning objectives for the fortnight, the teachers carefully considered where to build in opportunities for exploration. They then mapped out when each objective would be applied by the pupils, before filling in the details for key vocabulary and techniques.

It is impossible to capture the full complexity of how the purpose of the tasks develops over the ten lessons. However, the table opposite gives some idea. Although 'clarify' only appears once in the table, there are many concepts to clarify and skills to refine across this fortnight of learning. In general, clarification will not precede exploration (as this would reduce the opportunities for pupils to make sense of the mathematics for themselves), and the expectation would be that clarification is no longer required once pupils are asked to apply the concept or skill to an unfamiliar problem or context. Likewise, there is considerably more 'practice' taking place over the fortnight than can be indicated in the table.

Lesson	Purpose
1	*Measure angles on faces of 3D shapes* • **explore** angle measurement • **clarify** the names of 3D shapes
2	*Find out what's special about 360 and 180* • **practise** measuring angles • **explore** angle sums at a point and on a straight line
3	*Copy 2D representations of 3D shapes* • **apply** angle measurement, angle drawing and naming 3D shapes • **explore** angle drawing and 2D representations of 3D shapes
4	*Angles 2D, angles in 3D* • **practise** estimating and comparing angles, and naming 3D shapes
5	*Reasoning about rectangles* • **explore** reasoning about sides and angles in rectangles • **practise** angle sums at a point and on a straight line
6	*Draw regular polygons* • **explore** sides and angles in regular polygons • **practise** angle drawing and using angle facts - at a point and on a straight line
7	*Polygon puzzles* • **apply** angle fact identification • **practise** reasoning about lengths and angles in regular polygons
8	*Polygon puzzles* • **apply** angle fact identification • **practise** reasoning about lengths and angles in regular and irregular polygons
9	*Identify the mystery 3D shape given information about its faces or its 2D representation* • **apply** angle fact identification; reasoning about properties of rectangles and polygons
10	*Find missing angles and side lengths* • **apply** angle fact identification; reasoning about properties of regular and irregular polygons

Opportunities for fluency

Just as we do not expect all learning of English to happen during English lessons, we should expect the learning of mathematics to extend well beyond the mathematics lesson. Exploration, clarification, practice and application take time. Mastery does not happen in one individual lesson.

Clarification and practice of mathematical concepts and skills is most effective when it takes place over time. Sustained opportunities to practise help every child to become secure enough to be able to apply them to unfamiliar problems in new contexts.

Discussion points

• Does this plan offer enough opportunity for pupils to explore the concepts?
• Does this plan give time to clarification?
• Does this plan dedicate sufficient time to pupil practice?
• Does this plan offer pupils sufficient application?
• What would you do differently? Why?

Discussion points

Choose two or three weeks' worth of learning objectives for a class you teach.

1 *Exploration*

   Which of the objectives will pupils already have explored?

   Do you need to plan in exploration time for any of the objectives?

2 *Clarification*

   What are the common or potential misconceptions in this unit?

   Which concepts or skills require particular clarification?

   How will this be provided?

3 *Practice*

   Which concepts or skills require plenty of pupil practice?

   Can this be offered through exploration and application?

4 *Application*

   When in the unit will pupils apply each concept and skill?

   What opportunities can you offer for application, both within and beyond the mathematics lesson?

An important aspect of the mastery approach is the daily Maths Meeting. It is a ten to twenty minute whole-class session, used to consolidate key areas of mathematics. It includes singing, whole-class call and response together with 'hands-down' questioning where any child can be chosen to answer. This way, all pupils are fully involved.

Maths Meetings give the teacher opportunities to reinforce and check pupils' growing knowledge[1]. Perhaps more importantly, they are also thoroughly enjoyed by pupils.

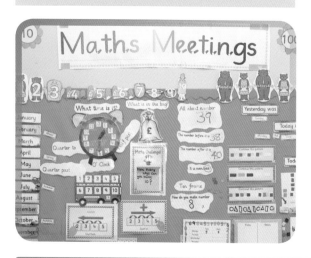

1 **Ofsted** (2014) *ARK Conway Primary Academy Inspection Report* URN: 137331. OfSTED Publications.

Case study – A Maths Meeting at King Solomon Academy

Teachers at King Solomon Academy use daily Maths Meetings to consolidate key ideas in mathematics, fill any gaps in understanding of mental arithmetic, and revise 'general knowledge mathematics' that may not be covered explicitly in units of work (such as months of the year, days of the week, etc.) Here is the story of one such session, with a class of five and six-year-olds.

Children are moved smoothly from their tables to the carpet whilst singing the 'Maths Song'. **Children are instantly engaged** and motivated and aware of the subsequent routine of the mathematics meeting. **The half hour session is separated into eight sections**, lasting between one minute and six minutes each.

Each section begins with a chant or song memorized by the children relevant to the learning they were about to embark on. No time is wasted at any point; all children know what to do and remain enthusiastic throughout. After this introduction to each section, children are asked to complete sentences such as:

"Today is ...."   "There are three more cool
                            days than hot days"

"Yesterday was ...."   "How many more?"

"Tomorrow will be...."   "Three more"

Full sentence responses are insisted on and a range of individual and whole class responses are expected. **All children are engaged at all times and the pace is snappy**.

The eight sections consist of key mathematical concepts that children need to know confidently in order to become competent mathematicians. They are as follows:

1 Months of the year

2 Days of the week

3 Bar charts (using weather descriptions as content)

4 Shapes

5 Patterns and sequences involving addition and subtraction

6 Money

7 Time

8 Place value

The questioning is a mixture of open and closed. The latter is to ensure fast pace and 100% knowledge and the more open-ended questions allow for explanatory responses (e.g. in section five, children are asked to explain *how they know* that the pattern was a 'plus 4' pattern).

The teacher moves effectively around the classroom **using a variety of resources** including the interactive whiteboard, magnetic coins for money and base-ten blocks. A key feature of the Maths Meeting is the **'Maths Meeting display'** which has posters to aid each section of learning.

The impact of using the **same structure** and resources each day ensures children learn knowledge partly through **repeated experience.** All children know key ideas and those who are less confident are identified by the teacher and asked to contribute, resulting in recognition for getting it right.

The Maths Meeting is a highly effective approach to engaging children in mathematics and revising key mathematical learning. Evidence shows that children at King Solomon Academy achieve well in mathematics; Maths Meetings appear to contribute to deep conceptual understanding.

Discussion points

- How would you introduce pupils to the songs and chants and 100% expectation?
- How long would it take for pupils to adopt these routines?
- How would you change the content of the Maths Meetings over time?
- How would you vary content between year groups?

> **"**We must all play our part to ensure that all our pupils receive the best possible mathematics education. **"**
>
> *Sir Michael Wilshaw*

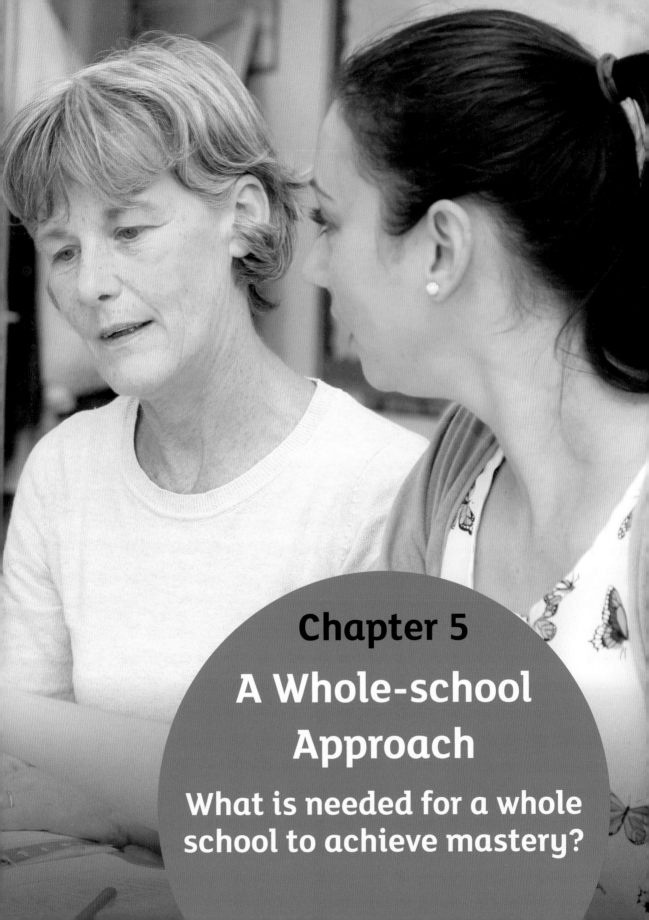

Chapter 5

A Whole-school Approach

What is needed for a whole school to achieve mastery?

What is needed for a whole school to achieve mastery?

For every pupil to have a genuine opportunity to master mathematics, teachers have an enormously complex role to play. This includes creating a positive classroom culture, having a sense of what pupils currently understand, and how they might understand it, and using this to inform next steps. This is a huge responsibility for any individual teacher, and it is therefore essential that society, parents, school leaders, and the wider education community do all they can to support them. Of course, one teacher can make a significant difference, but real transformation comes when teachers work together in collaboration across the school.

Schools can make a real difference. The Improving School Effectiveness Project in Scotland used value-added approaches to study eighty Scottish schools, and found that

"In terms of the progress gained,...the school has a greater influence than pupils' background characteristics such as age, gender or socio-economic disadvantage." [1]

Some schools were found to add significantly more value to their pupils than others (the school effect was greater in primary schools than in secondary schools, and more so in mathematics than in reading). So what makes some schools more effective than others?

In every school I've worked with where a high proportion of pupils have excelled in mathematics, the key to success has been whole-school leadership. In every case of a school transforming achievement in mathematics, they have exhibited strengths across the same five areas. In deriving the five levers for whole-school impact, I have drawn on the latest evidence, and worked with schools to review their approaches to leadership, professional learning and student learning. Clear messages are emerging from successful schools as to the leadership behaviours that lie behind their success.

1 MacBeath, J. and Mortimore, P. (eds.) (2001) *Improving School Effectiveness.* Buckingham: Open University Press. , p72.

Five levers for impact

Success with the mastery approach depends on the extent to which the whole school has:

- a **commitment to achievement** for every single pupil, no matter what their background or prior attainment
- clear, shared expectations around what they want **teaching** to look like, which are consistently adhered to when teaching is being **observed**
- high-quality, coherent opportunities for teachers to **learn and train**
- appropriate **resources** readily available and curriculum **structure** that makes time for mathematics
- consistent approaches across the curriculum, with **connections** made with other subjects, and pupil engagement, effort and progress **celebrated.**

These five levers that drive transformation align with those emerging from reviews of the literature. Viviane Robinson identifies five leadership practices associated with increased learning and well-being of students, in a meta-analysis of school leadership.[2] Four of these cohere closely with the whole-school framework developed with the Mathematics Mastery partner schools. They are:

- establishing goals and expectations (*commit & achieve*)
- resourcing strategically (*structure & resource*)
- ensuring quality teaching (*teach & observe*)
- leading teacher learning and development (*learn & train*)

The fifth mastery leadership lever, *connect & celebrate*, is particularly specific to mathematics, and so is not reflected in the meta-analysis. In its stead, their fifth practice is 'ensuring an orderly and safe environment'

Bill Mulford and colleagues find that there are three stages to schools becoming highly effective. First, school leaders develop a *community*, with a trusting and collaborative environment.[3] Secondly they add empowerment and a shared and monitored mission and practice, which leads to a *community of professionals*. Ultimately they build a *community of professional learners*, with supported collaborative experimentation.

3   **Mulford, B., Silins, H., & Leithwood, K.** (2004). *Educational leadership for organisational learning and improved student outcomes.* Dordrecht: The Netherlands: Kluwer.
Mulford, B., & Silins, H. (2011). Revized models and conceptualisation of successful school principalship that improves student outcomes. *International Journal of Educational Management,* 25(1), pp. 61–82.

2   **Robinson, V.** (2011). *Student-centered leadership.* San Francisco: Jossey Bass.

1. Commit and achieve

**Whole-school impact lever 1:
A *commitment to achievement* for every single pupil, no matter what their background or prior attainment**

A whole-school focus on achievement for every pupil has been shown to be vital in highly effective schools. Success doesn't just come from the belief that every child can achieve, it's about making sure that belief becomes a reality. Robust monitoring of the performance of individual pupils[4] and evaluation of school performance[5] have been shown to be important features of effective schools.

In working with schools to adopt the mastery approach, I find some teachers are understandably hesitant about the practicalities initially. In particular, some teachers are concerned that the mastery curriculum, where all children in a year group learn the same concepts and skills, will result in some children getting left behind, and others being held up. Provided the school leadership remains committed to differentiation through depth, over time teachers do realize that they can bring in additional challenges with the same concepts, so it really does impact each and every child. It takes time and effort for teachers to effectively differentiate for depth, and it is important that they are supported through this time of transformation.

Schools that have seen the greatest improvement in achievement through adopting a mastery approach have been those that explicitly make clear that the mastery curriculum is not 'just another scheme'. The headteacher, senior team and mathematics leader in these schools are passionate about the mastery approach, and it is this passion that enables them to change the minds of others in the school. This change of mindset comes about through leaders running training in staff meetings (see the *learn and train* section), and through leaders being in the classroom, teaching or team teaching (see the *teach and observe* section). What makes whole-school training effective is as much to do with its coherence and the continuity of its message over time as its content or delivery.

4   **Mortimore, P., Sammons, P., Stoll, L., Lewis, D., & Ecob, R.** (1988) *School matters: The junior years.* Salisbury: Open Books.
5   **Hargreaves, D. H. and Hopkins, D.** (1991) *The Empowered School: The Management and Practice of Development Planning,* London: Cassell.

Getting assessment right

Assessment is one of the most powerful tools we have as teachers. Awareness of children's current skills, knowledge and understanding is key to planning the next step in their learning. And yet a school's assessment system can often get in the way of transforming classroom practice.

Schools successfully teaching for mastery make sure that teacher assessment, and pupil self-assessment, are an integral part of every lesson. More formal assessments are planned two or three times a year, and these tests do not include concepts or skills with which the pupils are unfamiliar.

A particular challenge when introducing a curriculum, is the tension between assessing in a way that is aligned with the new curriculum, and assessing in a way that makes pupil attainment comparable with that of previous cohorts. Many of the schools I have worked with have navigated this by using curriculum-aligned assessments for weekly and half-termly checks, and national tests (or tests written in the style of national tests) termly or annually. This has enabled headteachers to be confident that children are making greater progress with the mastery approach than previous cohorts have done before its implementation.

Grouped for success

As discussed previously, high expectations for every child are quite simply incompatible with setting by 'ability'. As soon as children are grouped according to their perceived ability or potential, we place limitations on what some children can achieve. By teaching all children in the same year group the same mathematics, right from the start, we can ensure that every child is able to keep up, with no child left behind.

Discussion points

Is there a *commitment to achievement* for every single pupil, no matter their background or prior attainment?

- Is the headteacher fully informed about, and supportive of, a mastery approach to mathematics?
- Does the school's assessment in mathematics support a mastery approach?
- Does pupil grouping between and within classes support a growth mindset?
- Do approaches to intervention support a growth mindset?

2. Teach and observe

> **Whole-school impact lever 2:**
> **Clear, shared expectations around what *teaching* for mastery looks like, which are consistently adhered to when teaching is being *observed***

Teachers I've worked with have found that adopting a mastery approach in mathematics has had an effect on their teaching across all subjects. Headteachers have reported that their staff's lessons have become more confident and structured, and their teaching more purposeful. This transformation only comes about through leadership that emphasizes consistent application of certain features.

Ensuring teacher quality is second only to *leading teacher learning and development* in the effect it has on pupil achievement.[6] Having committed to a mastery approach, it is vital that schools establish clear, shared expectations around what great mathematics teaching looks like in their school context. Studies have shown the importance of the headteacher's role as 'leading professional', encompassing involvement in and knowledge about what goes on in the classroom, including the curriculum, teaching strategies, and monitoring pupil progress.[7] The evidence suggests that in schools where teachers report that their leadership is heavily involved in ensuring the quality of teaching, pupils do better.[8] This is not simply a matter of insisting on more classroom visits, teacher observations or more discussion of teaching and learning at staff meetings. More classroom visits and teacher feedback could make matters worse if the feedback was based on an inaccurate theory of teaching quality. School leaders need a defensible and shared theory of effective teaching that forms the basis of a coherent teaching programme in which there is collective rather than individual teacher responsibility for student learning and well-being.

An agreed understanding of mathematics teaching for mastery

Research evidence demonstrates that consistency of practice throughout the school has a positive impact on pupil progress.[9] In terms of the mastery approach, this means a consistent understanding of what constitutes deep understanding, and in particular:

- of the use of manipulatives
- of language
- of developing mathematical thinking.

6 Viviane Robinson's meta-analysis of research studies is described in **Robinson, V.** (2011). *Student-centered leadership.* San Francisco: Jossey Bass. **Robinson, V. M. J., Lloyd, C., & Rowe, K. J.** (2008). 'The impact of leadership on student outcomes: An analysis of the differential effects of leadership type.' *Educational Administration Quarterly,* 44(5), 635–674.

7 **Mortimore, P., Sammons, P., Stoll, L., Lewis, D., & Ecob, R.** (1988) *School matters: The junior years.* Salisbury: Open Books. **Rutter, M., Maughan, B., Mortimore, P., & Ouston, J.** (1979) *Fifteen thousand hours: Secondary schools and their effects on children.* London: Open Books.

8 **Robinson, V.** (2011). *Student-centered leadership.* San Francisco: Jossey Bass.

9 **Mortimore, P., Sammons, P., Stoll, L., Lewis, D., & Ecob, R.** (1988) *School matters: The junior years.* Salisbury: Open Books.

The importance of observation

Observation and feedback have been shown to be core features of effective professional development programmes.[10]

An example of one school's expectations of a mastery mathematics lesson is featured on page 80. It is important to develop your own guidelines to fit your particular school context but these can be used as a starting point.

Discussion points

In your school, are there clear, shared expectations around what *teaching for mastery* looks like, which are consistently adhered to when teaching is being *observed*?

- Do senior leaders regularly teach mathematics with a mastery approach?
- Is there a schedule of observations and clear guidelines for observation and feedback?
- Can all senior leaders explain expectations of mathematics teaching to external observers?

10 **Cordingley, P., Bell, M., Rundell, B., Evans, D.** (2003) The impact of collaborative CPD on classroom teaching and learning. In: *Research Evidence in Education Library*. London: EPPI-Centre, Social Science Research Unit, Institute of Education, University of London.

3. Learn and train

Whole-school impact lever 3: High-quality, coherent opportunities for teachers to *learn and train*

Professional development is the number one lever for transformation.

In comparing the impact of various efforts to improve pupils' mathematics achievement, including using new textbooks and classroom activities, teacher training, and interventions, Robert Slavin and colleagues find that professional development programmes have the strongest evidence of effectiveness.[11] School mathematics programmes that focused on changing daily teaching practice through professional development had a greater impact than with classroom materials alone.

Top performing countries place great emphasis on selecting and training teachers, prioritizing investment in teacher quality over reducing classroom sizes. Teachers in Shanghai are required to spend 180 hours on professional development over each five-year period of their career.[12] Chinese teachers' professional development is structured to ensure the consistency of student learner experiences.[13] Singapore, Sweden, and the Netherlands require at least 100 hours of professional development per year, in addition to the many hours spent in collaborative planning and inquiry.[14] In Singapore, mathematics teachers are expected to develop exemplary teaching by engaging in lesson study, action research, research project partnerships, and professional development activities organized by teachers and university academics.[15] For a real transformation in achievement, teachers and their school leaders need to make a really significant investment in professional development.

11 **Slavin, R.E., & Lake, C.** (2008), Effective programs for elementary mathematics: A best evidence synthesis. *Review of Educational Research,* 78 (3), 427–515.
Slavin, R.E., Lake, C., & Groff, C. (2009), Effective programs in middle and high school mathematics: A best evidence synthesis. *Review of Educational Research,* 79 (2), 839–911.

12 **Ingersoll, R.M.** (2007) *A Comparative Study of Teacher Preparation and Qualifications in Six Nations.* Consortium for Policy Research in Education.

13 **Liang, S., Glaz, S., DeFranco, T, Vinsonhaler, C, Grenier, R. & Cardetti, F.** (2013), 'An examination of the preparation and practice of grades 7–12 mathematics teachers from the Shandong Province in China', *Journal of Mathematics Teacher Education,* Vol. 16, pp. 149–160.

14 **Wei, R. C., Darling-Hammond, L., Andree, A., Richardson, N., Orphanos, S.** (2009) Professional learning in the learning profession: A status report on teacher development in the United States and abroad. Dallas, TX. National Staff Development Council.

15 **Kaur, B.** (2012) 'Nurturing excellence in mathematics instruction: Singapore's perspective', in Tai-Yih Tso (ed.), *Proceedings of the 36th Conference of the International Group for the Psychology of Mathematics Education,* Vol. 1, pp. 138–141. Taipei, Taiwan: PME.

Talking about teaching

Studies into effective professional development programmes have shown that many involve processes to encourage, extend and structure professional dialogue as well as ongoing collaborative working.[16]

When adopting a mastery approach, schools I have worked with have committed to at least an hour a week to engage in professional dialogue about teaching mathematics. Teachers often say this is the most significant difference their membership of the Mastery Partnership has made.

However, 'counting the PD hours' in this way may be an unhelpful way to think about professional development. Although, as teachers, we often limit the definition of 'professional development' to attendance at courses, conferences and INSET days, there is increasing evidence pointing to the importance of 'on-the-job' learning.[17]

It may be more helpful to consider professional development as encompassing all behaviours which are intended to effect change in the classroom.

Mathematics-specific pedagogy – learning to teach mathematics

For a successful whole-school approach, serious consideration must be given to teacher development that goes beyond training about general pedagogy, such as behaviour management, or about specific learner needs, or curriculum changes, or any of the

many other important areas that are relevant across the curriculum. Not only that, but this training must do more than simply develop teachers' mathematics subject knowledge. What is required is development of teachers' understanding of the *teaching of mathematics* – their mathematical 'pedagogical content knowledge'.[18] A big ask, especially given the many demands already fighting for teachers' time and attention.

Professional learning integrated into working life

One solution is to use teachers' usual working cycle of planning, teaching and reflecting on lessons as an opportunity for professional development. Rather than looking across a range of internet and paper-based resources each time a new topic is to be planned and taught, teachers can use this 'planning' time to learn more about the mathematical concepts involved, and the most effective ways to teach them.

Sustained and collaborative professional development has been shown to have a positive impact on teachers' range of teaching and learning strategies, and their ability to match these to their students' needs. The research literature on professional development shows the importance of involving teachers in applying and refining new knowledge and skills and experimenting with ways of integrating them in their day-to-day practice.[19] There is also some evidence that such professional development can result in a positive impact on student learning, motivation and outcomes.

16 **Cordingley, P., Bell, M., Rundell, B., Evans, D.** (2003) The impact of collaborative CPD on classroom teaching and learning. In: *Research Evidence in Education Library.* London: EPPI-Centre, Social Science Research Unit, Institute of Education, University of London.
17 See: **Edmonds, S. and Lee, B.** (2002) Teacher feelings about continuing professional development. *Education Journal, 61,* 28–29. **Hustler, D., McNamara, O., Jarvis, J., Londra, M., Campbell, A. and Howson, J.** (2003) *Teachers' Perspectives of Continuing Professional Development:* DfES Research Report No. 429, London: DfES. **Robinson, C. and Sebba, J.** (2004) *A Review of Research and Evaluation to Inform the Development of the New Postgraduate Professional Development Programme.* TTA / University of Sussex.

18 **Shulman, L. S.** (1987) 'Knowledge and teaching: Foundations of the new reform.' *Harvard Educational Review,* 57, 1–22. The quote can be found on page 8.
19 **Cordingley, P., Bell, M., Rundell, B., Evans, D.** (2003) The impact of collaborative CPD on classroom teaching and learning. In: *Research Evidence in Education Library.* London: EPPI-Centre, Social Science Research Unit, Institute of Education, University of London. **Cordingley, P., Bell, M., Evans, D., Firth, A.** (2005) The impact of collaborative CPD on classroom teaching and learning. Review: What do teacher impact data tell us about collaborative CPD? In: *Research Evidence in Education Library.* London: EPPI-Centre, Social Science Research Unit, Institute of Education, University of London. **Cordingley, P., Bell, M., Evans, D., Firth, A.** (2005) The impact of collaborative continuing professional development (CPD) on classroom teaching and learning. Review: How do collaborative and sustained CPD and sustained but not collaborative CPD affect teaching and learning? In: *Research Evidence in Education Library.* London: EPPI-Centre, Social Science Research Unit, Institute of Education, University of London.

Using specialist support

Studies indicate that professional development activity supported by specialists tends to have a positive impact for pupils.[20] This professional development generally builds on what teachers already know and can do, last at least two terms, and involves collaboration between teachers. The role of the specialist in such projects is to introduce the relevant knowledge base, and to model, observe, give feedback, coach, and discuss.

Discussion points

In your school, are there high-quality, coherent opportunities for teachers to *learn and train?*

- Does mathematics specific training align with other whole-school training initiatives?
- Are there formal and informal opportunities for staff to share ideas and strategies for effective mathematics teaching?
- Is lesson planning systematically used as a learning opportunity?
- Is specialist support made use of?

20 **Cordingley, P., Bell, M., Isham, C., Evans, D. & Firth, A.** (2007) What do specialists do in CPD programmes for which there is evidence of positive outcomes for pupils and teachers? London: EPPI-Centre, Social Science Research Unit, Institute of Education, University of London.

4. Structure and resource

Whole-school impact lever 4:
Appropriate *resources* readily available and curriculum *structured* to make time for mathematics

Schools that have successfully adopted a mastery approach to mathematics have invested significant resources into the implementation, and made timetabling and organizational decisions that prioritize mathematics.

Structural changes can make a real difference. Some credit structural differences, such as timetabling and the length of the school day, for the success of countries such as Singapore and Shanghai. In Shanghai, for example, mathematics is taught at the start of the day, so that work can be marked and intervention given the same day to children who need it. We may not have the luxury of daily non-contact time to review pupils' work, but we can still do same-day interventions.

Dedicating time to mastery

Teaching for mastery places more demands on curriculum time for mathematics than just an hour a day. For the whole class to develop a deep understanding of essential mathematical concepts, regular additional practice is required for all (in the form of daily Maths Meetings and other opportunities), and targeted intervention for many, as and when relevant.

Daily Maths Meetings

Schools that have transformed achievement through a mastery approach have allocated dedicated time on the school timetable for Maths Meetings. Their school leadership team are aware of when each year group is engaged in their Maths Meeting, and regularly pop in for monitoring, coaching, or to teach the meeting themselves! High-quality Maths Meetings have become embedded into the school culture.

Targeted intervention

The Williams Review strongly recommended early intervention for primary school children experiencing difficulties in mathematics.[21] In particular, it recommends that children with serious difficulties in mathematics should receive intensive one-to-one

21 **Williams, P.** (2008) *Independent Review of Mathematics Teaching in Early Years Settings and Primary Schools.* London: Department for Children, Schools and Families.

intervention from a qualified teacher, though paired or small group work may be appropriate in some instances.

Ann Dowker's research into intervention schemes found that individually targeted interventions appear worthwhile, demonstrating an impact on attainment.[22] The study emphasized the vital importance of appropriate management, guidance and training.

As the mastery curriculum works up through the school, intervention shifts from 'catching up' to 'keeping up'. Interventions work best when they are targeted on an individual child's weakness; the most efficient way of doing this is to directly tackle such 'weaknesses' as and when they crop up in the classroom.[23] From my experience of schools in the UK and abroad, the most effective interventions seem to be those that take place on the same day as the lesson.

This means finding creative ways to guarantee time for the teacher to work with a small number of pupils on mathematics *every day*. Several schools that I have worked with have arranged for a teaching assistant to supervise the class for ten to fifteen minutes each day while they engage in some independent learning such as reading or project work, freeing up the main class teacher to regularly lead the intervention.

Resourcing mastery

As emphasized in Chapter 3, hands-on experience with manipulatives alongside diagrams and symbols enables every child to gain a deep conceptual understanding. Classrooms must be well equipped with plentiful relevant resources. Without this, practicalities such as finding resources shared with another class, or organizing groups so that everyone can access a resource, can become barriers to their use.

Discussion points

In your school, are appropriate *resources* readily available and is the curriculum *structured* to make time for mathematics?

- Is the timetable reorganized to make time for Maths Meetings for every class, every day?
- Is spontaneous daily intervention planned for?
- Are appropriate concrete manipulatives available for every class?

22 **Dowker, A.** (2009) *What Works for Children with Mathematical Difficulties? The effectiveness of intervention schemes*. London: Department for Children, Schools and Families.
23 **Dowker, A.D.** (2004) *What Works for Children with Mathematical Difficulties?* London: DfES.

5. Connect and celebrate

Whole-school impact lever 5:
Consistent approaches across the curriculum, with *connections* made with other subjects, and pupil engagement, effort and progress *celebrated*

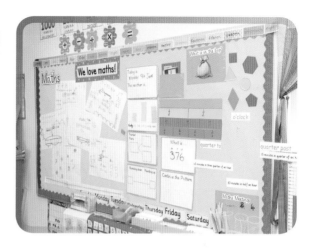

The final piece of this whole-school jigsaw lies in the way that what happens during mathematics lessons is connected with the rest of the school day, and with life at home. How is mathematics talked about? How are pupils' successes celebrated?

A growth mindset across the school

The cultural transformation required here must go beyond the mathematics classroom – the message that mathematical ability is not innate must be reinforced consistently throughout the school.

Practical ways of implementing this include:

● displaying pupils' mathematics successes publically in the school, e.g. by displaying photos of pupils using manipulatives

● adopting a shared language for praise across the school that focuses on effort and engagement

● training all adults in the school in the importance of talking positively about mathematics.

Getting parents involved

A 2003 review of relevant literature found that, "In the primary age range the impact caused by different levels of parental involvement is much bigger than differences associated with variations in the quality of schools.[24] The scale of the impact is evident across all social classes and all ethnic groups." So the impetus for increasing parental involvement is a strong one.

However, there are real barriers to such involvement. One significant one is the parents' own competence in and confidence with mathematics. In 1999, the Moser report found that approximately 20% of adults in England had severe literacy difficulties, whilst around 40% had problems with numeracy.[25] This is a particularly concerning statistic given that, when parents have better numeracy, their children also tend to have better numeracy.[26] Systematic literature

24 **Desforges, C. and Abouchaar, A.** (2003). *The Impact of Parental Involvement, Parental Support and Family Education on Pupil Achievement and Adjustment: A Literature Review.* Department of Education and Skills.
25 **DfEE** (1999) *Improving literacy and numeracy: A fresh start.* Great Britain Working Group on Post-School Basic Skills chaired by Sir Claus Moser. London: Department for Education and Employment.
26 **Carpentieri, J.D., Cara, O., & Litster, J.** (2013) *The Intergenerational Transfer of Numeracy Skills.* [IOE Research Briefing N°60] National Research and Development Centre for Adult Literacy and Numeracy commissioned by NIACE.
de Coulon, A., Meschi, E. & Vignoles, A. (2011): Parents' skills and children's cognitive and non-cognitive outcomes, Education Economics, DOI:10.1080/09645292.2010.511829.

review has found parental 'upskilling' in literacy and numeracy to be a necessary prerequisite to raising children's achievement.[27]

School-based programmes designed to support parents and carers in improving their children's attainment have been shown to have positive impact.[28] However, these involvement programmes are effective only when they include detailed and specific information about programmes and interventions, rather than more general attempts to supplement parental knowledge or change attitudes.[29]

For children to make exceptional progress in mathematics, their parents must be confident in their understanding of the mathematics their children are learning, as well as in the ways they are learning it. This enables them to discuss mathematics learning positively with their children, as well as to support them with their mathematics learning at home.

Schools adopting the mastery approach use a variety of initiatives to encourage learning at home. For example, they invite parents to join a mathematics lessons, to see for themselves how their children learn the subject, or hold Maths Meeting sessions for parents. Some schools have written parent guides to the mastery approach to teaching mathematics.

Parental support, and learning outside of school, may well contribute to pupil success, and efforts to involve parents can only be a good thing, but we should not despair if such support seems impossible to achieve in a given context. In my experience, schools in the most challenging of circumstances are able to transform achievement through transformational classroom teaching, even where parental involvement continues to be work in progress.

27 **Statham, J., Harris, A., Glenn, M. (with Morris, M., Marshall, H., Bergeron, C., White, K. and Mehta, P**. (2010) *Strengthening Family Wellbeing and Community Cohesion through the Role of Schools and Extended Services*. London: Centre for Excellence and Outcomes in Children and Young People's Services.

28 **O'Mara, A, Jamal, F, Lehmann, A & Cooper, C**. (2010) *Improving outcomes for young people by spreading and deepening the impact of targeted youth support and development* . London: Centre for Excellence and Outcomes in Children and Young People's Services (C4EO).
    Harris, A. and Goodall, J. (2008) "Do Parents Know They Matter? Engaging All Parents in Learning." *Educational Research* 50(3): 277 - 289.

29 **Hoover-Dempsey, K. V., Walker, J. M. T., Sandler, H. M., Whetsel, D., Green, C. L., Wilkins, A. S., and Closson, K.** (2005) 'Why do parents become involved? Research findings and implications.' *Elementary School Journal*, 106(2), 105–130.
    Moran, P. and Ghate, D. (2005).'The Effectiveness of Parenting Support.' *Children & Society* 19(4): 329–336.
    Centre for Community Child Health (2007) 'Parenting Young Children' (Policy Brief No. 9). Melbourne: Centre for Community Child Health.

Mathematics across the curriculum

There are two main reasons for embedding the learning of mathematics across the school curriculum. Firstly, pupils can explore and discover mathematical concepts in another subject, and begin to make sense of them for themselves before they are formally introduced to them in mathematics lessons. Secondly, concepts and skills that have been learnt in mathematics lessons can be applied in a wealth of contexts across the curriculum. It is vital that the school has a coherent, structured approach to the application of mathematics across the curriculum, in order that these two purposes do not become confused.

If children are expected to be familiar with a mathematical concept for application in another subject, but have not yet mastered that subject in mathematics, there is a likelihood of frustration and failure for both teacher and pupils alike. Similarly, the impact of a carefully planned experience in another subject that is designed to introduce children to a concept for the first time will be significantly reduced if the children have already worked with the concept in mathematics.

The placing of mathematics in 'relevant contexts' can be extremely positive, but only if it is done well.[30] The inclusion of some calculation work, say, during topic work on the Romans, will be positive only if it either offers pupils an opportunity to develop new calculation methods for themselves, or gives them an opportunity to efficiently and accurately use the calculation skills with which they are already familiar.

What might this look like in practice? A school might map key mathematics concepts across other subjects, indicating whether they have already been taught in mathematics lessons, or whether they will be first met in another subject. 'Maths Days' can be organized, where mathematics is celebrated across the school and included in all lessons throughout the day. Some schools include mathematics in whole school cross-curricular days. If following a mastery approach, it's important to ensure that the curriculum content for each year group is matched to the curriculum for depth.

Discussion points

In your school, are there consistent approaches across the curriculum, with *connections* made with other subjects, and pupil engagement, effort and progress *celebrated?*

- Is mathematics publically enjoyed and celebrated?
- Do rewards for mathematics celebrate how *effort* leads to learning?
- Do parents understand how mathematics is taught for mastery?
- Are parents involved in their children's mathematics learning?
- Are key mathematical concepts applied in other curriculum areas?

---

30 **Boaler, J.** (1993) 'The Role of Contexts in the Mathematics Classroom: do they make mathematics more real?' *For the Learning of Mathematics*, 13 (2) 12–17.

Leading a whole-school mastery approach – an action plan

The action plan below is designed to help you get started with, or further develop, the mastery approach. It gives twenty-five specific action points schools can take who want to take the next steps towards teaching for mastery.

Commit and achieve

Across the school, make a *commitment to achievement* for every single pupil, no matter what their background or prior attainment.

1   **Get informed** – before you start, the headteacher and senior team must be fully informed about, and supportive of, a mastery approach to mathematics, and must know the mathematics curriculum well.

2   Design or find an **assessment system** that supports a mastery approach. Know how you will monitor pupil progress and achievement, and how you will involve all adults in assessment. Be clear what success will look like.

3   Review **pupil grouping** with a growth mindset. Make sure that any grouping by 'prior attainment' is time-limited and has a clear purpose.

4   Plan for **intervention**. Make sure your approaches to intervention support a growth mindset – for example, targeted and focussed sessions for pupils identified using formative assessment, rather than fixed long-term intervention classes.

5   Make time to regularly **reflect on and review** current practice – challenge current practice and raise expectations.

Teach and observe

Develop clear, shared expectations around what *teaching for mastery* looks like, which will be consistently adhered to when teaching is being *observed.*

6   Agree **shared expectations** of what constitutes teaching mathematics for mastery across the school – agree how you will identify the impact of specific teaching techniques and approaches on pupils' learning.

7   Arrange for senior leaders and mathematics leads to regularly **teach mathematics** with a mastery approach.

8   Coordinate and encourage **peer observations** for teachers to learn from each other and provide a stimulus for professional discussions.

9   Upskill all staff so they can clearly **explain your school's expectations** of mathematics teaching with a mastery approach.

10   Agree how pupils' **progress will be recorded** in a way that informs next steps and provides useful feedback to pupils. This may include more creative evidence collection such as photographs, videos and pupils' reflections.

Learn and train

Plan high-quality, coherent opportunities for teachers to *learn and train.*

11 Consider your plans for **whole-school training** throughout the year. Think about how mathematics specific training will align with this for coherent messaging.

12 Ensure there is a **common understanding** of what 'differentiation for depth' means and looks like in practice.

13 Plan formal and informal opportunities for staff to **share ideas and strategies** for effective mathematics teaching. Consider how informal sharing of ideas and strategies will be promoted.

14 Make arrangements for collaborative **lesson planning** so that it can be systematically used as a learning opportunity by all teachers.

15 Support every adult and child in the school to consistently **use accurate and appropriate language** when talking about mathematics.

16 Make time to **keep up-to-date** with improvements and adaptations to the mastery approach to teaching mathematics, and to stay aware of relevant research.

Structure and resource

Make appropriate *resources* readily available and *structure* the curriculum to make time for mathematics.

17 Review the schools' supply and deployment of **concrete manipulatives**, so that the appropriate resources are available for every class, every lesson.

18 Reorganize the timetable to make time for **Maths Meetings** for every class, every day.

19 Schedule time for **daily intervention** to prevent gaps developing.

20 Ensure no time is wasted – adopt a **lesson structure** that makes every moment count.

Connect and celebrate

Plan consistent approaches across the curriculum, with *connections* made with other subjects, and pupil engagement, effort and progress *celebrated.*

21 Plan how you will publically enjoy and **celebrate mathematics** throughout the year, and make time for mathematical problem solving and application.

22 Check your **reward system** promotes a growth mindset and celebrates how *effort* leads to learning.

23 Consider how you will **inform parents** about your mastery approach to mathematics.

24 Plan **home-learning** opportunities that involve parents and encourage positive attitudes towards maths.

25 Map key mathematical concepts across **other curriculum areas** and plan connections.

Lesson observation guidelines

KEY ASPECTS	Teacher	Pupils
High expectations of engagement and attainment for every child	Conveys the message that progress is made through engagement and effort. Expects every pupil to succeed. Is enthusiastic about the learning expected. Gives **every** pupil the opportunity to experience or master key ideas.	Have high aspirations, believe they can achieve and work hard in order to do so. Want to learn and enjoy learning.
	Follows a mastery curriculum. Differentiates through scaffolding, questioning, and use of concrete and pictorial representations – instead of offering pupils different tasks. Uses speaking and listening activities, engaging resources and novel 'ways in' to a concept. Extends through further developing depth of language, conceptual understanding or mathematical thinking. Immediately acts on assessment from questioning and observation.	Explore mathematics and ask questions to deepen their appreciation of the subject. Are challenged by solving less routine problems, demonstrating using concrete manipulatives/ drawing diagrams, explaining in full sentences or asking their own questions.
Fewer topics, greater depth Depth of mastery for all	**Develops conceptual understanding** through multiple representations and connections. Has a full understanding where and why this lesson falls in the sequence and in the longer term development of pupils' mathematical understanding. Anticipates and incorporates misconceptions and inaccuracies.	Have access to concrete manipulatives. Manipulate objects or use pictorial representations to deepen their understanding. Make links between concrete, pictorial and abstract representations. Link new learning to previous learning in mathematics, other subjects and beyond school. Demonstrate conceptual understanding through tackling new problems.
	Develops communication of mathematical ideas, justifications and proofs Uses modelling to support pupils in developing independence in their mathematical recording. Considers own language and models expected language use clearly and accurately.	Participate in pair/group discussion tasks. Are ready to answer in class questioning/ discussion. Speak in full sentences. Use correct mathematical words and symbols. Use the key words.
	Develops mathematical thinking and ability to generalize Ensures every pupil participates in active thinking, through a variety of questioning techniques. Encourages use of independent learning strategies. Involves pupils in *generalizing* by comparing and classifying mathematical objects or talking about what might be sometimes, always or never true.	Do as much of the cognitive work – the writing, thinking, analyzing and talking – as possible. Seek general patterns and create examples.
Every opportunity is used to develop mathematical problem solving	Ensures that lesson **time is used purposefully.** Makes clear what pupils should be doing at every point on the lesson, so no time is wasted. Minimizes teacher talk.	Participate fully – everyone is engaged in the task. Collaborate, discussing their thinking. Work independently for some of the lesson. Demonstrate mastery and the ability to 'go it alone'.